Darwinism Comes to America

Primary Sources in
American History

CONSULTING EDITOR
Grady McWhiney, University of British Columbia

Darwinism
Comes to America

EDITED BY GEORGE DANIELS

Northwestern University

BLAISDELL PUBLISHING COMPANY
A Division of Ginn and Company

WALTHAM, MASSACHUSETTS / TORONTO / LONDON

Foreword

Thorough understanding of the events and trends that make up our history cannot be acquired merely by reading textbook interpretations. It is essential also to study the basis of such interpretations. *The Primary Sources in American History Series* provides the student with materials in the form of letters, diaries, memoirs, pamphlets, and newspaper accounts written during or shortly after major historical events — documents up to now buried in the library and often unavailable.

Edited and introduced by a leading scholar, each volume either concentrates on discussion of a given topic in contemporary letters, newspaper articles, and essays or presents new editions of classic eyewitness accounts of significant events. Though generations removed from an actual occurrence, the student has the opportunity to understand it in depth and to apply his analytical and critical powers to it. He then also can compare his own interpretations with those provided by general histories, biographies, and monographs.

GRADY MCWHINEY

Preface

The purpose of this volume is not to document the "impact" of evolutionary theory on American thought, or even on selected areas of American thought. Darwinism has been of such profound and continuing significance that one would be hard put to find a place to stop, and the covers of a book of moderate size could only contain part of the story. Its purpose is simply to illustrate the process — often painful — by which men come to terms with a major threat to their old patterns of thought. Reactions, of course, varied, and I have included only a few of them. Nevertheless, I think that there was a pattern underlying the developments of the first decade and a half of adjustment to the theory, and I think it likely that a similar pattern could be found in the reception of any other intellectual innovation which ramified to so many areas of thought and affected so many cherished beliefs of a society.

As one studies the fate of Darwin's theory in America nothing becomes more evident than the fact that the early story of Darwinian evolution was not simply one of accommodation of old ways of thought to a new truth of science. Rather the theory and the older ways of thought were made to accommodate themselves to each other. Neither made it through that period of adjustment unscathed. The theory suffered in this case, for the changes that were made in it were largely erroneous and soon repudiated. Nevertheless, the changes were probably essential during that difficult period of adjustment, for, without them, it is not likely that the theory would have been so quickly accepted. The modified view of evolution, which softened some of the more dismal aspects of Darwinism, made it possible for men to retain central portions of their older ways of thought.

In preparing this volume of readings, I have benefited from the advice of three Northwestern graduate students — Peter Carroll, Michael Fellman, and Anita Fellman — all of whom read the manuscript and offered suggestions, many of which I have adopted.

G. D.

Contents

Introduction

In the spring of 1859, after twenty years of thinking, observing, writing, and rewriting, the British naturalist Charles Darwin published what was to prove the most profoundly revolutionary book of his century. The book, bearing the laborious Victorian title *On the Origin of Species by Means of Natural Selection, or the Preservation of Favored Races in the Struggle for Life,* argued that, contrary to prevailing opinion, species of animal life were not fixed forever at the Creation. In place of this static conception, Darwin proposed that one species had developed out of another by a series of slow changes through countless eons of time. The process of change was essentially natural, requiring no creative interventions on the part of a Deity, and no miraculous works of any kind. If there had indeed been a Creation in the theological sense — and Darwin was inclined to believe that at the beginning the Creator might have "breathed life into" four or five forms at the most — it had occurred at some time in the dim past and was largely irrelevant as an explanation of the current life forms.

The publication of Darwin's elaborately documented argument provoked a major intellectual battle. A common reaction was that of Adam Sedgwick, a geologist and Darwin's former teacher, who dismissed the theory as "a dish of rank materialism cleverly cooked and served up merely to make us independent of a Creator." The American theologian Charles Hodge, in answer to his own question "What Is Darwinism?" stated flatly that "It is Atheism." Others, such as Thomas Henry Huxley, who became known as "Darwin's bulldog" for his vigorous championship of the theory, hailed it as man's liberation from metaphysical and theological dogma. To John Fiske, American historian, philosopher, and scientific popularizer, Darwinism was the crowning glory of the nineteenth century, which he characterized as the "period of the decomposition of orthodoxies." Still others — and their viewpoints are represented in the selections that follow — managed in varying ways to accommodate the new theory to their old ways of thought.

When Darwin wrote his book, the idea of evolution was already very old, and for certain limited purposes it had already attained respectability. By the early nineteenth century, historians, political theorists, and philosophers were making free use of evolutionary concepts in their speculative works; astronomers were articulating an evolutionary theory to explain the formation of the universe; and geologists were employing it to explain the formation of topographic features on the earth. Neither was the application to biology new, although earlier versions had not been considered respectable by the scientific community. The Frenchman Jean Baptiste Lamarck, half a century earlier, and the Scot Robert Chambers, only fifteen years before Darwin, had published books defending evolutionary theories of the development of animal species. Indeed, Darwin's own grandfather, Erasmus Darwin, had published poetic versions of a theory of biological evolution before the beginning of the nineteenth century.

Darwin's contribution to this line of thought was a massive array of evidence to support the fact of evolution and, even more importantly, a unifying hypothesis that explained how evolution had taken place. It was the mechanism that Darwin placed greatest emphasis upon, and it was this element that

ultimately compelled belief. Natural selection, Darwin's term
for the mechanism of evolution, was based on four broad principles, all of which Darwin had borrowed and combined in a
unique pattern which he thought could explain all of organic
nature.

1. In any given area a great many more life forms come into
existence than the environment could possibly support. If all
the fish eggs, for example, were allowed to hatch and grow to
maturity, the rivers, lakes, and oceans of the world would very
soon be unable to hold them. Even elephants, the slowest
breeding of all animals, would soon overpopulate the earth,
Darwin calculated, if they remained unchecked. This idea was
a generalization of Malthus's* argument that population always
grows faster than the food supply. Where Malthus and the
classical economists had used this principle mainly to explain
why the conditions of the working classes could never rise
above the subsistence level, Darwin saw that it had broader
possibilities. Such a prodigality of life, he argued, would lead
to a struggle for existence in which only the fittest would
survive. Darwin used the word "struggle" in a very broad
sense — actual cases of conflict among individuals, he thought,
were comparatively unimportant. The more meaningful
struggle was the effort to gain food, to protect oneself from
the weather, or to procreate. The giraffe, for example, with a
slightly longer neck than his fellows, would be able to gather
leaves from higher limbs and would thus have an advantage in
the "struggle for existence."

2. From the moment of their birth, no two organisms are
exactly alike. There are minute, random variations among
individuals, even of the same species, *and these variations can*

---

* Thomas Robert Malthus (1766–1834) was a British economist best
known for his theory of population summarized in the formula: "Population grows geometrically, food supply grows arithmetically." The
tendency, therefore, will always be for living standards to be depressed
toward the subsistence level.

be transmitted by heredity. Darwin, of course, like everyone else of his time, had no idea how heredity operated. The concept of the gene was still nearly a half century in the future. Darwin simply postulated heredity as a fact of observation which could not, for the moment, be explained any more than could the origin of variation.

3. In the struggle among unlike individuals, those differences which are advantageous, however minute, will enable their possessors to survive. Those lacking the desirable characteristic will be unable to meet the exigencies of the environment, and will die out, leaving few or no offspring.

4. The winners in the struggle for existence will transmit their characteristics by heredity. Given enough time, an accumulation of minor modifications will finally result in the formation of a new species and the evolutionary struggle will begin again with some other favorable variation.

Clearly, if time is not limited, and if variation is indeed infinite, Darwin's theory could explain the entire biological past — from the one-celled organism all the way through man. The cumulative effect of minute variations over vast stretches of time could be called upon to explain the development of any given structure — say, an eye, a wing, or a webbed foot. But just as important, from the point of view of natural science, was the ability of natural selection to account for the present admirable adaptation of animal species to the conditions of their existence. Naturalists had long insisted upon the *fact* of adaptation; that is, they knew that each species was especially suited for the inorganic environment in which it lived — be it hot, cold, dry or humid — and they knew that animals were provided with appropriate mechanisms for escaping their enemies, securing their food, and perpetuating their species. There had even been extensive studies of internal adaptation which had revealed a general harmony of construction, a suitability of each organ for its function, and a co-adaptation of various organs and parts. This knowledge had been extremely useful to paleontologists in reconstructing fossils, and for systematists in classification. But earlier naturalists had adopted the supernaturalistic explanation offered by natural theologians for this marvelous adaptation. Suitability of organs for function, and of the whole animal for its conditions of existence, they argued, implied conscious design, and a design implies a designer; therefore, adaptation must be the direct work of a Creator. The question was thus effectively removed from the realm of natural science. The very fact that it was cold in the Arctic Circle, for example, was an adequate explanation for the unusually heavy bodily covering provided by God for those animals destined to pass their lives there. The whole work of nature was a supreme testimony to the wisdom and benevolence of God; adaptation was therefore not a matter for science to be especially concerned about.

Darwin, however, applied to these same facts a naturalistic explanation which entirely removed the need for intervention by any Designer. When conditions remain constant, he argued, animals and plants naturally do not depart from their well-adapted type, for variations which make the organism less suited for the environment will place the possessor at a disadvantage in the struggle for existence. But when conditions change, some of the naturally-occurring variations will prove better suited to the new conditions; such favorable variations will be selected for preservation — much the way a breeder selects from his breeding stock characteristics which please him — and the organisms will change. The change, of course, since it has no external direction, will be slow and gradual, but if continued over eons of geological time, it will produce any degree of alteration. Thus the theory can account for slight differences between related genera and species as well as the long continued trends revealed by geological history.

The magnificent sweep, and yet the utter simplicity, of the theory was awe-inspiring. Bold and comprehensive as it was, it had the virtue of apparent obviousness once it was stated.

"How extremely stupid not to have thought of that," was Huxley's initial reaction, and he later declared himself ready to go to the stake for the theory.

Had witch-burning still been in vogue, however, there were others who probably would have been pleased to send Huxley to the stake for his enthusiasm. It was difficult to be neutral about Darwinism, and the zealous defenders of Darwin made neutrality even more difficult; for every day, so it seemed, came notice of a new area of thought that was threatened by the theory. The study of linguistics quickly became an evolutionary science, then anthropology, sociology, philosophy, and one could go on down the list until he arrived at theology itself, which some thinkers soon began to suggest could use a dose of evolutionary theory. Nothing seemed safe to the worried defenders of tradition, and after a brief period of indulgent ridicule in the hope that Darwinism, like other fads, would soon pass away if it were not taken seriously, the forces of tradition launched all-out attacks from many directions.

Although there is an obvious threat to the religious view of life in such a purely natural explanatory hypothesis of biological evolution, it is important to recognize that the Darwinian conflict was not simply another chapter in the "conflict between science and religion." The issues were not nearly so clear as that. On the contrary, there was a wide range of views on Darwinism, within both science and religion, ranging from complete, unthinking rejection through caution to complete, unthinking acceptance.

The harshest religious critics would have nothing to do with the theory, arguing that there was a "polar opposition," between Darwinism and Biblical truth, and that "Adam and Christianity must stand or fall together." "If Darwin is right," said another, "the Bible is wrong." It is easy to understand their concern, for Darwin permitted naturalists to use the "wise contrivances" of nature, and the old theological concepts of purpose and final cause, not as explanations as the earlier naturalists did, but simply as indications of where to look for

the mechanical connections underlying the evolutionary process. The simultaneous appearance of evolutionary theory and
historical or anthropological critiques of Biblical concepts, and
the obvious relation of these studies to one another, aggravated
the religious problems. However, the insistence on the part of
these critics that one could not accept the teachings of science
and still remain faithful to the precepts of Christianity was
probably unfortunate for all sides, for it made the final acceptance of science more difficult, and subsequently it made the
position of religion more insecure once evolution was accepted
by scientists.

The mind of man, however, is infinitely complex. Many,
whose religious convictions were no doubt as sincere as those
of the critics, welcomed the theory with open arms. By these
people, Darwinism was generally interpreted teleologically —
that is, they insisted that the process Darwin had described was
simply another instance of the infinitely "wise contrivance" of
nature; that the evolutionary process, including natural selection, had been directed by the Creator toward some beneficent
end. The stream of variation, as a prominent American botanist was fond of saying, had been directed, much as a river is
directed on its course. Beginning with such an argument, one
could find a variety of consolations and virtues in evolution
that had not been dreamed of even in natural theology. One
clergyman, for example, was converted on the grounds that it
opened up new and more glorious prospects for immortality;
others declared themselves ready to give up the old doctrine
of the "fall of man" in favor of the happier idea of a gradual
and unceasing progress to a higher physical and spiritual state
— finding in Darwinism confirmation of the idea of progress.
One distinguished botanist bewildered Darwin by declaring
himself a convert on the grounds that the theory finally made
intelligible the birth of Christ and redemption by grace. It
was not even necessary to interpret Darwinism teleologically
to find religious meaning in it. Some Calvinists gloried in it
because, so they thought, it exalted chance, not design, leaving

room for the unpredictability of the Creator's ways. American theologian George F. Wright, for example, suggested that Darwinism was to natural science as Calvinism was to theology — a foe to sentimentalism and optimism, a check on the reign of law and the trust in reason.

Scientists, for their part, exemplified the same range of opinions. To Louis Agassiz, one of America's most distinguished naturalists, it was a "mere mine of assertions" without the slightest foundation, and he declared, in what was one of the rashest predictions of his time, that "I shall outlive this mania." His Harvard colleague, Asa Gray, an early champion of the theory, adopted its essentials immediately, but remained wary of the extreme lengths to which some were taking it. Others, impressed by the explanatory power of the theory, tried to generalize from it to areas far beyond biology. University of Cincinnati professor F. W. Clarke, for example, noting the regularity of atomic weights, concluded that elements with such regularity must be results of an evolutionary process. A number of other scholars published erudite studies of the "evolution of language," by which they did not mean merely the development of one language out of another, but a crudely animistic "struggle for existence" among words.

Still further from the biological process that the theory had been formulated to explain were the great number of cosmic generalizations erected upon its basis, by Charles Sanders Pierce, John Fiske and others. The "Social Darwinism" that such a generalization often led to is well known, thanks to a study by Richard Hofstadter. The most common understanding of "Social Darwinism" is the one identified by Hofstadter, and that best represented by William Graham Sumner. By locating the struggle for existence among human beings in the open competition of the marketplace, Sumner derived a philosophy of extreme individualism, of laissez faire in economics and government. In society, as in nature, there was presumed to be a "natural order" which, left alone, would ensure the "survival of the fittest." Any interference with that order, either to direct the organization of society or to protect special interest, would violate nature and therefore enfeeble society.

Those who arrived at such a conclusion thought about the struggle for existence and survival of the fittest on an individual basis, but actually it was not necessary to do so; and Sumner was practically alone in the pessimistic conclusions which he reached. Just as logical, for example, was Lester Frank Ward who, by locating the struggle between species rather than among the individuals of one species, was able to transform the same principle of struggle into a justification for the welfare state. Neither was Karl Marx being less logical when he enthusiastically declared the *Origin* to be "a basis in natural science for the class struggle in history." Marx was so impressed that he presented Darwin a complimentary copy of his *Capital*, and later offered to dedicate the English translation to him — an honor which the naturalist modestly declined.

The impact of the theory was such that few areas of thought could remain unaffected by it. Whether one accepted the theory or rejected it, he still had to take account of it in some way. The precise way in which men did take account of it, however, varied in terms of individual training, prepossessions, and special interests, as well as in terms of individual interpretations of either the threat or the promise of the theory. This volume, which takes the story down to about 1880, contains only a few of the infinitely varied reactions to what was undoubtedly the most profound intellectual innovation of modern times.

GEORGE DANIELS

The Theory
Comes to
America

In America, as in England, the theory provoked bitter controversies — somewhat delayed, to be sure, by the fact of a Civil War and the all-encompassing importance of politics during the first five years after Darwin's book appeared. After the initial reviews, and the discussions before a number of scientific and literary societies, little attention was paid to Darwinism until well after the end of the war. Only a handful of papers appeared on what seemed to be a Darwinian basis, and the theory was rarely mentioned. The initial comments, however, were a portent of things to come.

The earliest champion of Darwin in America was Asa Gray, a Harvard professor of botany, an editor of the influential *American Journal of Science and Arts,* and one of the most celebrated scientists in the country. Gray had bitterly attacked earlier evolutionary theories, but his studies of plant geography during the 1850's prepared him for a friendly reception of Darwin's concept of natural selection when it was first broached to him in a letter from Darwin written in July 1856. This letter was shortly followed by a draft of a paper outlining the argument that was later to appear in the *Origin of Species.* Gray therefore became the first man outside a small circle of English naturalists to be admitted to Darwin's confidence. Although Gray remained a devout Presbyterian, certain that science and his faith could not clash, he had no use for the "theological scientists" like Agassiz,* who refused to admit the possibility of evolution. Once he had assured a "fair hearing" for the theory of natural selection, Gray devoted his life to popularizing his view of the bearing of evolution on religious thought.

The major selection reprinted here is a masterful account of the theory, a statement of its difference from earlier theories, particularly that of Agassiz, and an effort to calm the fears of those who would be offended by its evident naturalism. In a spirit of fairness, Gray also pointed out the obvious scientific objections to the theory. Throughout the review, he deliberately adopted the tone of one who, although not fully convinced, was inclined toward the theory. Noting that natural selection "chimes in with the established doctrines of physical science," Gray suggested, with what was to prove singular prescience, that the doctrine was likely to be accepted long before it could be proved.

During the spring of 1860, Darwinism was the subject of a number of debates at the Boston Society of Natural History and at the American Academy of Arts and Sciences, which also met at Boston. Since the same individuals generally attended meetings of both societies, I have arranged the extracts from reports of both meetings in chronological order, to illustrate better the continuing argument. Asa Gray's generally technical remarks at the meetings have been omitted, for they consisted mostly of elaboration of points made in his review.

---

* Jean Louis Rodolphe Agassiz (1807–1873), a Swiss-born naturalist with an international scientific reputation, came to the United States in 1845 and soon became the most popular scientist in the country. Firmly committed to his own views of the doctrine of special creation, Agassiz never accepted evolution. His particular arguments against Darwin, however, reveal no understanding of the principle of natural selection. As John Fiske later suggested, it is doubtful that he ever really bothered to read Darwin carefully, for his assumption that evolutionary divergence, if it had occurred, should be measured in terms of overall "progress" would have been better applied to Lamarck's work than to Darwin's.

Not even the dry, terse, and unemotional language adopted by the secretaries in reporting the debates is able to conceal the highly-charged atmosphere that probably prevailed in Boston during that momentous spring. It was in the course of discussions such as these, and through newspaper accounts of such meetings, that Americans first became acquainted with the theory. The discussants, for the most part, are feeling their way cautiously about the theory, trying to make up their own minds concerning its implications for them.

C. DARWIN

Letter to Asa Gray, *Francis Darwin* (ed.), *The Life and Letters of Charles Darwin*
New York, D. Appleton and Company, 1897, 1, pp. 437–438

Down, July 20th [*1856*]

. . . It is not a little egotistical, but I should like to tell you (and I do not *think* I have) how I view my work. Nineteen years (!) ago it occurred to me that whilst otherwise employed on Nat. Hist., I might perhaps do good if I noted any sort of facts bearing on the question of the origin of species, and this I have since been doing. Either species have been independently created, or they have descended from other species, like varieties from one species. I think it can be shown to be probable that man gets his most distinct varieties by preserving such as arise best worth keeping and destroying the others, but I should fill a quire if I were to go on. To be brief, I *assume* that species arise like our domestic varieties with *much* extinction; and then test this hypothesis by comparison with as many general and pretty well-established propositions as I can find made out, — in geographical distribution, geological history, affinities, &c., &c. And it seems to me that, *supposing* that such hypothesis were to explain such general propositions, we ought, in accordance with the common way of following all sciences, to admit it till some better hypothesis be found out. For to my mind to say that species were created so and so is no scientific explanation, only a reverent way of saying it is so and so. But it is nonsensical trying to show how I try to proceed in the compass of a note. But as an honest man, I must tell you that I have come to the heterodox conclusion that there are no such things as independently created species — that species are only strongly defined varieties. I know that this will make you despise me. I do not much underrate the many *huge* difficulties on this view, but yet it seems to me to explain too much, otherwise inexplicable, to be false. . . .

*　*　*

I must say one word more in justification (for I feel sure that your tendency will be to despise me and my crotchets), that all my notions about *how* species change are derived from long-continued study of the works of (and converse with) agriculturists and horticulturists; and I believe I see my way pretty clearly on the means used by nature to change her species and *adapt* them to the wondrous and exquisitely beautiful contingencies to which every living being is exposed. . . .

ASA　GRAY
Letter to Charles Darwin, *Jane L. Gray (ed.), Letters of Asa Gray London, Macmillan and Company, 1893, II, pp. 457–458*

Cambridge, January 23, 1860

MY DEAR DARWIN, —

*　*　*

To fulfill your request, I ought to tell you what I think the weakest, and what the best, part of your book. But this is not easy, nor to be done in a word or two. The best part, I think, is *the whole*, that is, its plan and treatment, the vast amount of facts and acute inferences handled as if you had a perfect mastery of them. I do not think twenty years too much time to produce such a book in. . . .

* * *

Then your candor is worth everything to your cause. It is refreshing to find a person with a new theory who frankly confesses that he finds difficulties, insurmountable at least for the present. I know some people who never have any difficulties to speak of.

The moment I understood your premises, I felt sure you had a real foundation to hold on. Well, if one admits your premises, I do not see how he is to stop short of your conclusions, as a probable hypothesis at least.

It naturally happens that my review of your book does not exhibit anything like the full force of the impression the book has made upon me. Under the circumstances I suppose I do your theory more good here, by bespeaking for it a fair and favorable consideration, and by standing noncommitted as to its full conclusion, than I should if I announced myself a convert; nor could I say the latter, with truth.

Well, what seems to me the weakest point in the book is the attempt to account for the formation of organs, the making of eyes, etc., by natural selection. Some of this reads quite Lamarckian.*

The chapter on Hybridism is not a *weak*, but a *strong* chapter. You have done wonders there. But still you have not

---

* Jean Baptiste Lamarck (1774–1829) was a French zoologist who argued in his *Philosophie Zoologique* (1809) that species evolved because changes in an organism during its lifetime were transmitted to its offspring. These changes resulted indirectly from the influence of the environment in stimulating habits of use and disuse. According to Lamarck, the environment was not seen as a mechanically causal force; the *effort* of the organism as it responded to challenges or possibilities offered by the environment was the determining force. Some Lamarckian elements, as Gray perceived, were taken over by Darwin and incorporated into his theory.

accounted, as you may be held to account, for divergence up
to a certain extent producing increased fertility of the crosses,
but carried one short, almost imperceptible, step more, giving
rise to sterility, or reversing the tendency. Very likely you are
on the right track; but you have something to do yet in that
department. . . .

A S A   G R A Y
Review of Darwin's Theory on the Origin of Species by Means of
Natural Selection, *American Journal of Science*, 2nd ser., XXIX,
March, 1860, 153–184

The ordinary and generally received view assumes the
independent, specific creation of each kind of plant and animal
in a primitive stock, which reproduces its like from generation to generation, and so continues the species. Taking the
idea of species from this perennial succession of essentially
similar individuals, the chain is logically traceable back to a
local origin in a single stock, a single pair, or a single individual, from which all the individuals composing the species
have proceeded by natural generation. Although the similarity
of progeny to parent is fundamental in the conception of
species, yet the likeness is by no means absolute: all species
vary more or less, and some vary remarkably — partly from
the influence of altered circumstances, and partly (and more
really) from unknown constitutional causes which altered
conditions favor rather than originate. But these variations
are supposed to be mere oscillations from a normal state, and
in Nature to be limited if not transitory; so that the primordial
differences between species and species at their beginning have
not been effaced, nor largely obscured, by blending through
variation. Consequently, whenever two reputed species are
found to blend in nature through a series of intermediate
forms, community of origin is inferred, and all the forms, however diverse, are held to belong to one species. Moreover, since

bisexuality is the rule in Nature (which is practically carried out, in the long run, far more generally than has been suspected), and the heritable qualities of two distinct individuals are mingled in the offspring, it is supposed that the general sterility of hybrid progeny, interposes an effectual barrier against the blending of the original species by crossing.

From this generally accepted view the well-known theory of Agassiz and the recent one of Darwin diverge in exactly opposite directions.

That of Agassiz differs fundamentally from the ordinary view only in this, that it discards the idea of a common descent as the real bond of union among the individuals of a species, and also the idea of a local origin, — supposing, instead, that each species originated simultaneously, generally speaking, over the whole geographical area it now occupies or has occupied, and in perhaps as many individuals as it numbered at any subsequent period.

Mr. Darwin, on the other hand, holds the orthodox view of the descent of all the individuals of a species not only from a local birth-place, but from a single ancestor or pair; and that each species has extended and established itself, through natural agencies, wherever it could; so that the actual geographic distribution of any species is by no means a primordial arrangement, but a natural result. He goes farther, and this volume is a protracted argument intended to prove that the species we recognize have not been independently created, as such, but have descended, like varieties, from other species: species are varieties of a larger growth and a wider and earlier divergence from the parent stock: the difference is one of degree, not of kind.

The ordinary view—rendering unto Caesar the things that are Caesar's—looks to natural agencies for the actual distribution and perpetuation of species, to a supernatural for their origin.

The theory of Agassiz, referring as it does the phenomena both of origin and distribution directly to the Divine will, —

thus removing the latter with the former out of the domain of inductive science (in which efficient cause is not the first, but the last word), — may be said to be theistic to excess. The contrasted theory is not open to this objection. Studying the facts and phenomena in reference to proximate causes, and endeavoring to trace back the series of cause and effect as far as possible, Darwin's aim and processes are strictly scientific, and his endeavor, whether successful or futile, must be regarded as a legitimate attempt to extend the domain of natural or physical science. For though it well may be that "organic forms have no physical or secondary cause," yet this can be proved only indirectly, by the failure of every attempt to refer the phenomena in question to causal laws. But, however originated, and whatever be thought of Mr. Darwin's arduous undertaking in this respect, it is certain that plants and animals are subject from their birth to physical influences, to which they have to accommodate themselves as they can. How literally they are "born to trouble," and how incessant and severe the struggle for life generally is, the present volume graphically describes. Few will deny that such influences must have gravely affected the range and the association of individuals and species on the earth's surface. Mr. Darwin thinks that, acting upon an inherent predisposition to vary, they have sufficed even to modify the species themselves and produce the present diversity. Mr. Agassiz believes that they have not even affected the geographical range and the actual association of species, still less their forms; but that every adaptation of species to climate and of species to species is as aboriginal, and therefore as inexplicable, as are the organic forms themselves. . . .

*   *   *

We have contrasted these two extremely divergent theories, in their broad statements. It must not be inferred that they have no points nor ultimate results in common.

In the first place they practically agree in upsetting, each in its own way, the generally received definition of species, and in sweeping away the ground of their objective existence in Nature. The orthodox conception of species is that of lineal descent: all the descendants of a common parent, and no other, constitute a species; they have a certain indentity because of their descent, by which they are supposed to be recognizable. So naturalists had a distinct idea of what they meant by the term species, and a practical rule, which was hardly the less useful because difficult to apply in many cases, and because its application was indirect, — that is, the community or origin had to be inferred from the likeness; that degree of similarity, and that only, being held to be conspecific which could be shown or reasonably inferred to be compatible with a common origin. And the usual concurrence of the whole body of naturalists (having the same data before them) as to what forms are species attests the value of the rule, and also indicates some real foundation for it in nature. But if species were created in numberless individuals over broad spaces of territory, these individuals are connected only in idea, and species differ from varieties on the one hand and from genera, tribes, &c. on the other only in degree; and no obvious natural reason remains for fixing upon this or that degree as specific, at least no natural standard, by which the opinions of different naturalists may be correlated. Species upon this view are enduring, but subjective and ideal. Any three or more of the human races, for example, are species or not species, according to the bent of the naturalists's mind. Darwin's theory brings us the other way to the same result. In his view, not only all the individuals of a species are descendants of a common parent but of all the related species also. Affinity, relationship, all the terms which naturalists use figuratively to express an underived, unexplained resemblance among species, have a literal meaning upon Darwin's system, which they little suspected, namely, that of inheritance. Varieties are the latest offshoots of the genealogical tree in "an unlineal" order; species, those of an earlier date, but of no definite distinction; genera, more ancient species, and so on. The human races, upon this view likewise may or may not be species according to the notions of each naturalist as to what differences are specific: but, if not species already, those races that last long enough are sure to become so. It is only a question of time. . . .

* * *

It may also be noted that there is a significant correspondence between the rival theories as to the main facts employed. Apparently every capital fact in the one view is a capital fact in the other. The difference is in the interpretation. . . .

* * *

[*There follows an extract from Agassiz's* Essay on Classification *which Gray uses to illustrate Agassiz's theological interpretation of the facts used by Darwin in his theory of natural selection.*]

In a word, the whole relations of animals, &c. to surrounding nature and to each other, are regarded under the one view as ultimate facts, or in their ultimate aspect, and interpreted theologically; — under the other as complex facts, to be analyzed and interpreted scientifically. The one naturalist, perhaps too largely assuming the scientifically unexplained to be inexplicable, views the phenomena only in their supposed relation to the Divine mind. The other, naturally expecting many of these phenomena to be resolvable under investigation, views them in their relations to one another, and endeavors to explain them as far as he can (and perhaps farther) through natural causes. . . .

* * *

That the existing kinds of animals and plants, or many of them, may be derived from other and earlier kinds, in the lapse of time is by no means a novel proposition. Not to speak of ancient speculations of the sort, it is the well-known Lamarckian theory. The first difficulty which such theories meet with is that, in the present age, with all its own and its inherited prejudgments, the whole burden of proof is naturally, and indeed properly laid upon the shoulders of the propounders; and thus far the burden has been more than they could bear. From the very nature of the case, substantive proof of specific creation is not attainable; but that of derivation or transmutation of species may be. He who affirms the latter view is bound to do one or both of two things. Either, 1, to assign real and adequate causes, the natural or necessary result of which must be to produce the present diversity of species and their actual relations; or, 2, to show the general conformity of the whole body of facts to such assumption, and also to adduce instances explicable by it and inexplicable by the received view, — so perhaps winning our assent to the doctrine, through its competency to harmonize all the facts, even though the cause of the assumed variation remain as occult as that of the transformation of tadpoles into frogs. . . .

* * *

The first line of proof, successfully carried out, would establish derivation as a true physical theory; the second, as a sufficient hypothesis. . . .

* * *

Mr. Darwin attempts both lines of proof, and in a strictly scientific spirit; but the stress falls mainly upon the first; for, as he does assign real causes, he is bound to prove their adequacy. . . .

* * *

Having conceived the idea that varieties are incipient species, he is led to study variation in the field where it shows itself most strikingly and affords the greatest facilities to investigation. Thoughtful naturalists have had increasing grounds to suspect that a re-examination of the question of species in zoology and botany, commencing with those races which man knows most about, viz. the domesticated and cultivated races, would be likely somewhat to modify the received idea of the entire fixity of species. This field, rich with various but unsystematized stores of knowledge accumulated by cultivators and breeders has been generally neglected by naturalists, because these races are not in a state of nature; whereas they deserve particular attention on this very account, as experiments, or the materials for experiments, ready to our hand.* In domestication we vary some of the natural conditions of a species, and thus learn experimentally what changes are within the reach of varying conditions in nature. We separate and protect a favorite race against its foes or its competitors, and thus learn what it might become if nature ever afforded it equal opportunities. Even when, to subserve human uses, we modify a domesticated race to the detriment of its native vigor, or to the extent of practical monstrosity, although we secure forms which would not be originated and could not be perpetuated in free nature, yet we attain wider and juster views of the possible degree of variation. . . .

*　*　*

In this way races arise, which under favorable conditions may be as hereditary as species. In following these indications, watching opportunities, and breeding only from those individuals which vary most in a desirable direction, man leads the course of variation as he leads a streamlet, — apparently at will, but never against the force of gravitation, — to a long distance from its source, and makes it more subservient to his use or fancy. He unconsciously strengthens those variations which he prizes when he plants the seed of a favorite fruit, preserves a favorite domestic animal, drowns the uglier kittens

---

* There is good reason to believe that the work of Gregor Mendel, completed in the 1860's, but largely ignored by the scientific world until its "rediscovery" in 1900, was so casually dismissed by scientists precisely because the objects of his studies (garden peas) were not in a state of nature. It would be interesting to know what Gray, who saw the fallacy in this objection, would have thought of Mendel's work had he seen it. There is no evidence that either Gray or Darwin knew of the Austrian monk's experiments.

of a litter, and allows only the handsomest or the best mousers to propagate. Still more, by methodical selection, in recent times almost marvelous results have been produced in new breeds of cattle, sheep, and poultry, and new varieties of fruit of greater and greater size or excellence. . . .

* * *

Some suppose that races cannot be perpetuated indefinitely even by keeping up the conditions under which they were fixed: but the high antiquity of several, and the actual fixity of many of them, negative this assumption. "To assert that we could not breed our cart and race horses, long and short-horned cattle, and poultry of various breeds, for almost an infinite number of generations would be opposed to all experience." . . .

* * *

We see everywhere around us the remarkable results which Nature may be said to have brought about under artificial selection and separation. Could she accomplish similar results when left to herself? Variations might begin, we know they do begin, in a wild state. But would any of them be preserved and carried to an equal degree of deviation? Is there anything in nature which in the long run may answer to artificial selection? Mr. Darwin thinks that there is; and Natural Selection is the key-note of his discourse. . . .

* * *

In applying his principle of natural selection to the work in hand, Mr. Darwin assumes: 1, some variability of animals and plants in nature; 2, the absence of any definite distinction between slight variations, and varieties of the highest grade; 3, the fact that naturalists do not practically agree and do not increasingly tend to agree, as to what forms are species and what are strong varieties, thus rendering it probable that there may be no essential and original difference, or no possibility of ascertaining it, at least in many cases; also, 4, that the most flourishing and dominant species of the larger genera on an average vary most (a proposition which can be substantiated only by extensive comparisons, the details of which are not given); — and, 5, that in large genera the species are apt to be closely but unequally allied together, forming little clusters around certain species, — just such clusters as would be formed if we suppose their members once to have been satellites or varieties of a central or parent species, but to have attained at length a wider divergence and a specific character. The fact of such association is undeniable; and the use which Mr. Darwin makes of it seems fair and natural.

The gist of Mr. Darwin's work is to show that such varieties are gradually diverged into species and genera through natural selection; that natural selection is the inevitable result of the struggle for existence which all living things are engaged in; and that this struggle is an unavoidable consequence of several natural causes, but mainly of the high rate at which all organic beings tend to increase.

Curiously enough, Mr. Darwin's theory is grounded upon the doctrine of Malthus and the doctrine of Hobbes. The elder de Candolle had conceived the idea of the struggle for existence and in a passage which would have delighted the cynical philosopher of Malmesbury, had declared that all nature is at war, one organism with another or with external nature, and Lyell and Herbert had made considerable use of it.* But

---

* Thomas Hobbes (1588–1679), an English philosopher, was one of the first to attempt to apply to man the same principles of physical science which govern the rest of the material world. In his *Leviathan* (1651) and other works, he argued that the fear of men for each other was the basis of state sovereignty. Augustin Pyrame de Candolle (1778–1841) was a Swiss botanist who proposed a system of classification based on "natural relationships" among species. Sir Charles Lyell (1797–1875) was the author of *Principles of Geology* (1830–1833) which explained the present structure of the earth as a result of the uniform action of the regular forces of nature acting over immense periods of time, an evolutionary conception of the earth's formation. Edmond Herbert (1812–1890) was a French geologist who had done extensive work on fossils in chalk deposits.

Hobbes in his theory of society and Darwin in his theory of natural history alone have built their systems upon it. However moralists and political economists may regard these doctrines in their original application to human society and the relation of population to subsistence, their thorough applicability to the great society of the organic world in general is now undeniable. And to Mr. Darwin belongs the credit of making this extended application, and of working out the immensely diversified results with rare sagacity and untiring patience. He has brought to view real causes which have been largely operative in the establishment of the actual association and geographical distribution of plants and animals. In this he must be allowed to have made a very important contribution to an interesting department of science, even if his theory fails in the endeavor to explain the origin or diversity of species. . . .

*   *   *

[*Gray then passes to objections to Darwin's theory, the most evident of which is the absence of intermediate forms in the fossil record.*]

He is confident that intermediate forms must have existed; that in the olden times when the genera, the families and the orders diverged from their parent stocks, gradations existed as fine as those which now connect closely related species with varieties. But they have passed and left no sign. The geological record, even if all displayed to view is a book from which not only many pages, but even whole alternate chapters have been lost out, or rather which were never printed from the autographs of nature. The record was actually made in fossil lithography only at certain times and under certain conditions (i.e., at periods of slow subsidence and places of abundant sediment); and of these records all but the last volume is out of print; and of its pages only local glimpses have been obtained. Geologists, except Lyell, will object to this, — some of them moderately, others with vehemence. Mr. Darwin himself admits, with a candor rarely displayed on such occasions, that he should have expected more geological evidence of transition than he finds, and that all the most eminent palaeontologists maintain the immutability of species.

The general fact, however, that the fossil fauna of each period as a whole is nearly intermediate in character between the preceding and the succeeding faunas, is much relied on. We are brought one step nearer to the desired inference by the similar "fact, insisted on by all palaeontologists, that fossils from two consecutive formations are far more closely related to each other, than are the fossils of two remote formations. . . ."

*   *   *

We pass to a second difficulty in the way of Mr. Darwin's theory; to a case where we are perhaps entitled to demand of him evidence of gradation like that which connects the present with the tertiary mollusca. Wide, very wide is the gap, anatomically and physiologically (we do not speak of the intellectual) between the highest quadrumana and man; and comparatively recent, if ever, must the line have bifurcated. But where is there the slightest evidence of a common progenitor? Perhaps Mr. Darwin would reply by another question: where are the fossil remains of the men who made the flint knives and arrowheads of the Somme valley? . . .

*   *   *

[*Gray's third point has to do with the sterility of hybrids; this was once thought to be a formidable objection to all descent theories.*]

A fourth and the most formidable difficulty is that of the production and specialization of organs.

It is well said that all organic beings have been formed on two great laws: Unity of type, and Adaptation to the conditions of existence. The special teleologists, such as Paley*, occupy themselves with the latter only; they refer particular facts to special design, but leave an overwhelming array of the widest facts inexplicable. The morphologists build on unity of type, or that fundamental agreement in the structure of each great class of beings, which is quite independent of their habits or conditions of life; which requires each individual "to go through a certain formality," and to accept, at least for a time, certain organs, whether they are of any use to him or not. Philosophical minds form various conceptions for harmonizing the two views theoretically. Mr. Darwin harmonizes and explains them naturally. Adaptation to the conditions of existence is the result of Natural Selection; Unity of type, of unity of descent. Accordingly, as he puts his theory, he is bound to account for the origination of new organs, and for their diversity in each great type, for their specialization, and every adaptation of organ to function and of structure to condition, through natural agencies. Whenever he attempts this he reminds us of Lamarck, and shows us how little light the science of a century devoted to structural investigation has thrown upon the mystery of organization. Here purely natural explanations fail. The organs being given, natural selection may account for some improvement; if given of a variety of sorts or grades, natural selection might determine which should survive and where it should prevail. . . .

*   *   *

We are thus, at last, brought to the question; what would happen if the derivation of species were to be substantiated either as a true physical theory, or as a sufficient hypothesis?

---

* William Paley (1743–1805), was the author of *View of the Evidences of Christianity* (1794), an elaborate presentation of the argument from design. Comparing the world to an intricately designed watch, Paley argued that the existence of such a mechanism compelled men to believe in an intelligent designer, analogous to the watchmaker.

What would come of it? The enquiry is a pertinent one, just now. For, of those who agree with us in thinking that Darwin has not established his theory of derivation, many will admit with us that he has rendered a theory of derivation much less improbable than before; that such a theory chimes in with the established doctrines of physical science, and is not unlikely to be largely accepted long before it can be proved. Moreover, the various notions that prevail, — equally among the most and the least religious, — as to the relations between natural agencies of phenomena and Efficient Cause, are seemingly more crude, obscure, and discordant than they need be.

It is not surprising that the doctrine of the book should be denounced as atheistical. What does surprise and concern us is, that it should be so denounced by a scientific man,* on the broad assumption that a material connection between the members of a series of organized beings is inconsistent with the idea of their being intellectually connected with one another through the Deity, i.e., as products of one mind, as indicating and realizing a preconceived plan. An assumption the rebound of which is somewhat fearful to contemplate, but fortunately one which every natural birth protests against.

It would be more correct to say, that the theory in itself is perfectly compatible with an atheistic view of the universe. That is true; but it is equally true of physical theories generally. Indeed, it is more true of the theory of gravitation, and of the nebular hypothesis, than of the hypothesis in question. The latter merely takes up a particular, proximate cause, or set of such causes, from which, it is argued, the present diversity of species has or may have contingently resulted. The author does not say necessarily resulted; that the actual results in mode and measure, and none other must have taken place. On the other hand the theory of gravitation, and its extension in the nebular hypothesis, assumes a universal and ultimate physical cause, from which the effects in nature must necessarily

---

* Agassiz.

have resulted. Now it is not thought, at least at the present day, that the establishment of the Newtonian theory was a step towards atheism or pantheism. Yet the great achievement of Newton consisted in proving that certain forces, (blind forces, so far as the theory is concerned,) acting upon matter in certain directions, must necessarily produce planetary orbits of the exact measure and form in which observation shows them to exist; — a view which is just as consistent with eternal necessity, either in the atheistic or the pantheistic form, as it is with theism.

Nor is the theory of derivation particularly exposed to the charge of the atheism of fortuity; since it undertakes to assign real causes for harmonious and systematic results. . . .

*　　*　　*

In our opinion, then, it is far easier to vindicate a theistic character for the derivative theory, than to establish the theory itself upon adequate scientific evidence. Perhaps scarcely any philosophical objection can be urged against the former to which the nebular hypothesis is not equally exposed. Yet the nebular hypothesis finds general scientific acceptance, and is adopted as the basis of an extended and recondite illustration in Mr. Agassiz's great work.

How the author of this book harmonizes his scientific theory with his philosophy and theology, he has not informed us. Paley, in his celebrated analogy with the watch, insists that if the time-piece were so constructed as to produce other similar watches, after the manner of generation in animals, the argument from design would be all the stronger. What is to hinder Mr. Darwin from giving Paley's argument a further a-fortiori extension to the supposed case of a watch which sometimes produces better watches, and contrivances adapted to successive conditions, and so at length turns out a chronometer, a town clock, or a series of organisms of the same type? From certain incidental expressions at the close of the volume, taken in connection with the motto adopted from

Whewell,* we judge it probable that our author regards the
whole system of Nature as one which had received at its first
formation the impress of the will of its Author, foreseeing the
varied yet necessary laws of its action throughout the whole
of its existence, ordaining when and how each particular of the
stupendous plan should be realized in effect, and — with Him
to whom to will is to do — in ordaining doing it. Whether
profoundly philosophical or not, a view maintained by eminent philosophical physicists and theologians, . . . will hardly
be denounced as atheism. Perhaps Mr. Darwin would prefer
to express his idea in a more general way, by adopting the
thoughtful words of one of the most eminent naturalists of
this or any age, substituting the word action for "thought,"
since it is the former (from which alone the latter can be inferred) that he has been considering. "Taking nature as exhibiting thought for my guide, it appears to me that while
human thought is consecutive, Divine thought is simultaneous,
embracing at the same time and forever, in the past, the present, and the future, the most diversified relations among hundreds of thousands of organized beings, each of which may
present complications again, which, to study and understand
even imperfectly, — as for instance man himself — mankind
has already spent thousands of years." In thus conceiving of
the Divine Power in act as coetaneous with Divine Thought,
and of both as far as may be apart from the human element of
time, our author may regard the intervention of the Creator
either as, humanly speaking, done from all time, or else as
doing through all time. In the ultimate analysis we suppose
that every philosophical theist must adopt one or the other
conception.

A perversion of the first view leads towards atheism, the
notion of an eternal sequence of cause and effect, for which

---

* William Whewell (1794–1866) was an English philosopher of science
who argued that God brought about natural events by the establishment
of general laws, not by "insulated interpositions of Divine power."
Whewell, however, did not accept Darwinism.

there is no first cause, — a view which few sane persons can long rest in. The danger which may threaten the second view is pantheism. We feel safe from either error in our profound conviction that there is order in the universe; that order presupposes mind; design, will; and mind or will, personality. Thus guarded, we much prefer the second of the two conceptions of causation, as the more philosophical as well as Christian view, — a view which leaves us with the same difficulties and the same mysteries in Nature as in Providence, and no other. Natural law, upon this view, is the human conception of continued and orderly Divine action.

We do not suppose that less power, or other power, is required to sustain the universe and carry on its operations, than to bring it into being. So, while conceiving no improbability of "interventions of Creative mind in nature," if by such is meant the bringing to pass of new and fitting events at fitting times, we leave it for profounder minds to establish, if they can, a rational distinction in kind between His working in nature carrying on operations, and in initiating those operations. . . .

*　*　*

The work is a scientific one, rigidly restricted to its direct object; and by its science it must stand or fall. Its aim is, probably not to deny creative intervention in nature, — for the admission of the independent origination of certain types does away with all antecedent improbability of as much intervention as may be required, — but to maintain that Natural Selection in explaining the facts, explains also many classes of facts which thousand-fold repeated independent acts of creation do not explain, but leave more mysterious than ever. How far the author has succeeded, the scientific world will in due time be able to pronounce. . . .

*　*　*

The Debates in Boston, *Proceedings of the Boston Society of Natural History, VIII, 1859–1861, pp. 231–235, 241–245, 250–252, 271–273, 274–275;* and *Proceedings of the American Academy of Arts and Sciences, 1857–1860, pp. 410–416.*

February 15, 1860 (Boston Society)

Prof. Agassiz made a verbal communication in opposition to the theory of Mr. Darwin, recently put forth in his work on the origin of species. Mr. Darwin he acknowledged to be one of the best naturalists of England, . . . but this great knowledge and experience had, in the present instance, been brought to the support, in his opinion, of an ingenious but fanciful theory. . . . He did not think it fair to compare the present fauna of the world with the fauna of any geological horizon as known in one locality; and he thought this method of comparison had led to this idea of gradual development. Animal representatives were as numerous and diversified in early geological periods as now, he instanced the brachiopods . . . [in which] there is an unbroken succession of *lingulae* up to the Jurassic strata; . . . in the lowest cretacean (neocomian) they appear again, then there is an interruption until the Tertiary epoch. . . . He thought the persistence of this form through so extensive a period, the last no more perfect than the first, was a fatal objection to the theory of gradual development.

Prof. Rogers* . . . thought that Darwin would meet such objections by the fact that the vital characters of some animals

---

* William Barton Rogers (1804–1882) was a prominent geologist, whose chief work was a study of the structure of the Appalachian chain, in collaboration with his brother, Henry Darwin Rogers. In 1861, William B. Rogers was a leader in establishing the Massachusetts Institute of Technology. Both William and Henry Rogers had been evolutionists since at least the early 1840's.

fit them for resisting change and extinction better than more plastic natures; from our knowledge of domesticated animals we find that dogs have changed very much, and that cats have changed hardly at all; some have great energy of resistance, and some very little. He adduced several cases of interruption, . . . which he explained by migrations to and from a given region. . . . He thought these evidences of migration, and not in the least degree of sudden creation without previous parents; the *lingula* hiatus suggests a similar abandonment and return of allied species in remote geological epochs. In the case of *Calymene Blumenbachii*, which extends from the lower Silurian up to the Devonian, there is a great variety of forms acknowledged to be within the limits of one species, displaying a progressive variation amounting almost to specific difference. It may also be a question whether the geological horizon of animal origin has yet been reached in our investigations. He inquired of Prof. Agassiz if any vertebrate had ever been found in strata lower than the upper Silurian.

Prof. Agassiz remarked, as to these alleged migrations, that we know that species are well circumscribed within the limits of faunae; and that before such a line of argument can be followed, it must be shown that any species pass from one continent to another, except from man's agency. In regard to the geological horizon of animal origin, he observed that the azoic system of rocks is not so metamorphosed as not to show traces of fossils if they had existed; fragments at least would be found; yet these rocks immediately underlie the Silurian strata rich in fossils. He thought that in this lowest system of fossils there was such a coordination of the animal series as shows that all its great and principal classes were then existing. . . . Trilobites are found in the lowest beds; these are complicated animals, and belong among the highest crustaceans; in the three other great divisions of the animal kingdom it is not the lowest, but the highest representatives that are found; the earliest fishes are among the most perfect of their class, and have many reptilian characters; the mollusks belong to the high cephalopods, and the crinoids rank high among the echinoderms. In the late general works, eleven or twelve subdivisions of the earth's crust are given . . . but he was prepared to show the occurrence of at least forty-eight successive periods of change, with characteristic fossils found neither below nor above their respective beds; the alleged identity of fossils in different strata was only apparent, and would be found so on actual comparison of specimens.

Mr. Emerson* asked what had been the antecedents to the publication of the work on the "Origin of Species." He did not quite understand the attitude of the mind of the author; he thought that the mind of an investigator into the laws of nature ought to be judicial, prepared to weigh impartially the evidence afforded by all the facts, and to let the balance incline accordingly. But Darwin comes before the reader at once as an advocate of a seemingly foregone conclusion, and argues, not for the purpose of finding in what direction the evidence of any particular fact would lead the mind, but for the purpose of finding something in the fact favorable to his preconceived opinion. Admitting the difficulties in his theory, he tries to explain them away by various suppositions and *ifs*, which by frequent repetition and consideration seem in the mind of the author to become established truths, and are used as arguments.

Prof. Rogers stated in reply that the present work of Darwin is a *résumé* of his conviction on the subject, without the presentation of the facts upon which it rests, which he has not had time to arrange. The problem is admitted to be of transcendent

---

* George B. Emerson (1797–1881), an educator and educational leader, was an old-school naturalist whose major scientific work was *Report on the Trees and Shrubs Growing Naturally in the Forests of Massachusetts* (1846). Earlier, he had served as President of the Boston Society of Natural History (1837–1843). Note his appeal to a literal-minded empiricism in order to argue against Darwin's method of reasoning. This was an issue that would arise many times in the future.

difficulty, and such as no observer or theorist can hope now or perhaps ever positively to resolve. Mr. Darwin makes no pretensions to an absolute demonstration, but, after an impartial survey of the facts bearing on the subject and a candid appreciation of the opposing considerations, adopts the view set forth in his book, as offering, in his opinion, a more rational and satisfactory explanation of the history of living nature than the hypothesis of innumerable successive creations. Prof. Rogers regarded the work as marked in an extraordinary degree by fairness in the statement of opposing as well as favorable arguments, by the absence of dogmatism, and by all other evidences of a truth-loving spirit, as well as by the extent and variety of its knowledge and the breadth of its philosophical views.

As regards the statement that the most ancient types of life were higher or more perfect than recent ones, . . . [Rogers] remarked that the term "perfection" is just as indefinite as the word "species." He considered perfection as specialization in each type; if an animal approach nearer perfection because, for instance, it be part fish and part reptile, or if a structure part animal and part vegetable be more perfect than the plant, then is the cell the type of perfection, combining as it does properties belonging to both kingdoms; he considered perfection, not the union of different types, but specialization in each particular type.

Prof. Agassiz considered perfection to mean an embodiment of the highest combinations, the most complex representation of life. The embryo fish presents features of its type superior to those of the adult fish; the tendency to specialization increases with its growth, and the animal at last becomes only a fish, losing its embryonic type of the higher vertebrates. As a generalization or philosophic conception, the vertebrate egg is superior to man himself, inasmuch as it embodies all that may be produced from it. . . .

* * *

[*March* 7, *1860*]

Prof. Agassiz made a communication on consecutive faunae and their corresponding number of geological formations, as furnishing arguments against the theory of Darwin.

He believed that the number was considerably greater than had been hitherto admitted. He objected to the use made of the great and well-known changes in animals under the influence of domestication, as an argument in favor of similar probable changes in geological ages; the genera of these domesticated animals, . . . lived ages before the human period, but their remains show no such changes as now occur; these are two distinct series of facts, and are not comparable. The representatives of these faunae* differ specifically, and do not pass from one to the other, and this is true from the most ancient to the most recent periods. . . . Faunae differ in various parts of the world, and no one can be taken as a type of existing creation; for instance, the fauna of Canada differs entirely from that of Africa, and any zoologist who should take one or the other or any single fauna as the type of the world's animals would commit an absurdity; yet geologists do this constantly in their identifications of geological periods, and of course fall into the gravest errors. He found fault with the methods of determining the limits of successive faunae usually pursued by geologists; he thought that this order should be determined by the fossils; that the rocks should be regarded merely as the tombs of the fossils, that naturalists should try to find out the animals of an epoch, and establish the limits of faunae on zoological and not on physical principles. . . .

*   *   *

Prof. Rogers replied that the entire severance of these faunae must be demonstrated, before such a line of reasoning

---

* Agassiz defined faunae as groups of animals enclosed within circumscribed areas.

can be employed against the theory of Darwin; if such a distinction be true, we must abandon nearly all the hitherto accepted specific determinations of other accomplished zoologists, most of whom maintain that animal forms do pass from one stratum to another. The division lines, moreover, are essentially local; the number of species said to pass from one formation to another may be so great in some localities as entirely to obliterate divisions which in other and not very remote places are marked by very sharp transitions. . . .

* * *

[*Rogers gives some examples from recent geological works in New York and Canada, showing the differing distribution of species.*]

Seeing, then, that faunae are not unfrequently mingled in contiguous formations, that they do not hold the same precise geological level or vertical distribution at different localities, that they may even become inverted in relation to each other, offering in this and other cases evidence of emigration and remigration in successive times, Prof. Rogers maintained that the *precise and absolute limitation* of faunae to formations, as advocated by Prof. Agassiz, if true in any case, is at best but of local and partial application, and can not be the basis of a palaeontological arrangement of formations. Even according to the ordinary and much less stringent view of geological faunae, it is found that only the few great divisional lines of the geological column are persistent over extensive areas, while the numerous subordinate ones, however distinct at the typical locality, lose themselves as they are traced, to give place to other modes of subdivision.

As regards the comparison of the tertiary fossils with corresponding modern forms, [Rogers said] . . . the likeness becomes extremely close as we approach the modern epoch, and this would seem to lend support to Mr. Darwin's doctrine of

modification by natural selection. In regard to the discrimi-
nation of species, the question at last must come to this: What is
the limit of specific difference? who shall be the arbiter? what
[is] the principle of distinction between species and variety,
and what [is] the guide in drawing the lines of demarcation of
the successive faunae?

Prof. Agassiz remarked that he did not expect the immediate
reception of his views, though convinced that they were true,
but believed that after mature examination of his facts they
would be generally received. . . . He did not think that the
increasing acknowledged differences point in any way to a
gradation of species or to a confusion of animal forms, but
rather enable the naturalist to distinguish clearly his species.
He alluded to chemistry, in which there was a time when
platinum and other silver-like metals were not distinguished
from silver; but in the progress of science they were ascertained to be separate and distinct species.

Prof. Rogers replied that this argument would answer
equally well for the other side of the question; for instance,
chemistry has reduced to one many supposed different species,
as the diamond, plumbago, and carbon. . . .

*   *   *

[*March 21*]

Prof. Agassiz continued his remarks on the subject of successive faunae, of which he considered there were more than fifty,
capable of as satisfactory proof in geological periods as at the
present day, and at least ten more indicated.

His object at the present time was not to explain the origin
and connection of faunae; we must take them as we find them,
as matters of fact, without reference now as to how they were
produced.* It is important in the discussion of this subject to
bear in mind that some faunae are strictly defined, while others

---

* Note that Agassiz, as Gray charged, consistently denied the legitimacy
of even inquiring into origins.

run together; there is very great difference in this respect; Mr. Wallace,* a strong advocate of Darwin's theory, admits the remarkable limitation between the Australian and Indian Archipelago faunae, separated by a strait only fifteen miles wide, yet, with the exception of a few birds, entirely distinct. Faunae are not necessarily, therefore, like each other because near together, nor unlike because widely separated; the former is shown by the case just cited, in which there is complete distinction, though circumstances favor a mingling of faunae; on the other hand, those of widely distant Africa and the east coast of America between the tropics are very much alike. These do not look like migrations, which are at best limited, and in which, if the conditions of life were much changed, the animals would be destroyed; marine animals, in an element which invites migration, are very much circumscribed within limits as to depth of water, and could not migrate from one part of the world to another across ocean abysses. Another obstacle in the way of migration is the transfer of progeny; eggs in most animals cannot bear much change of temperature or of location, without destruction of the contained embryo. . . .

[*March 27, 1860, AAA&S*]

Mr. J. A. Lowell, Professor Bowen, and Professor Agassiz discussed adversely the hypothesis of the origin of species through variation and natural selection. . . .

*   *   *

Mr. Lowell suggested that the supposed varieties in the vegetable kingdom were the result of hybridation. He also criticised the hypothesis in question on scientific and philosophical grounds, and condemned its tendency.

---

* Alfred Russel Wallace (1823–1913), an English naturalist and philosopher, independently formulated the principle of natural selection. He and Darwin presented their papers jointly before the Linnaean society in 1858, although Wallace never attempted to deprive Darwin of primary credit. Wallace later became a leading exponent of the "Neo-Darwinian" school of thought.

Professor Bowen* raised similar objections; contending that this hypothesis is one of cosmogony rather than of natural history, and makes such huge demands upon time, that the indefinite becomes virtually infinite time, so rendering the theory dependent on metaphysical rather than inductive reasoning; he denied the validity of all reasoning from the variability of plants to that of animals, or that the two had enough in common to warrant inferences from the one to the other; he also denied the variability of instinct in any animals, or that there was any evidence of the heritability of variations of structure or instinct except in a few sporadic cases, and in these only for two or three generations. He insisted that there was no reason why, on the theory, instinct and structure should vary contemporaneously; and finally he maintained that the theory denied the doctrine of the permanence of type, as received by all naturalists, was incompatible with the whole doctrine of final causes, and negatived design or purpose in the animate or organic world. . . .

*   *   *

Professor Parsons† made a communication upon the general subject. He remarked that: —

The new theory rested wholly on the assumption that the changes or variations by which the author supposed that species were established, were always minute, and effected

---

* Francis Bowen (1811–1890), was Alford Professor of natural religion, moral philosophy and civil polity at Harvard. He was a prominent logician whose chief interest was in the problem of harmonizing philosophy with Christianity. In 1851, Bowen had gained the distinction of being the only man in history who lost a Harvard appointment because of his conservatism. His attack on Kossuth and the Hungarian revolution caused the trustees to withdraw his appointment as McLean Professor of history.

† Theophilus Parsons (1797–1882) was a professor in the Harvard law school, well known legal writer, and amateur cultivator of natural history. His effort, in the following passage, to substitute mutations for minute variations was specifically rejected by Darwin when he read Parsons' paper.

their purpose only by accumulation through ages. But Mr. Parsons regarded this as wholly unnecessary. The records of monstrosity show that aberrant variation, in the direction of loss or degradation, may go very far indeed. And we have no reason whatever for holding it to be a law, that aberrant variation may not, possibly, in some instances, go equally far in the direction of gain and improvement. Supposing this to be possible, we reconcile the theories of Darwin and Agassiz. Admitting all the new creations which Agassiz requires, the question then occurs, How are these creations created? We must choose, either chance, and chance is a word only and not a thing, or creation at once out of nothing, by creative will; or from earth and water and chemical elements summoned to a proper place, at a proper time, in proper proportions, by the same exertion of Omnipotence. One of these we *must* choose, or else accept the theory that these new creations were created by means of some influence of variation exerted upon the ovum of some existing kindred creature, either before or at conception, or during uterine nutriment. This last supposition Mr. Parsons deemed by far the most reasonable and philosophical. Thus, if we suppose that the time had come for a dog to exist for the first time, and become the father of all dogs, it is far easier to believe that he was born of a wolf, a fox, a hyena, or a jackal, than that he suddenly flashed into existence out of nothing, or from a few pounds of chemical elements. Mr. Parsons then remarked upon some of the facts in geology that seem to favor this view; particularly the noticeable circumstance, that, as the great classes of animals succeed each other, they are not separated by periods of nothingness, but lap over each other, and are joined by connecting links. . . . And in the same connection, Mr. Parsons adverted to the singular fact, that man, who begins in the uterus as a nucleated cell, or monad, on his way to birth puts on the traces and characteristic indications of all the great families of animals. Asserting that the time had come when science must either adopt the doctrine of creation out of nothing, or else admit that new creatures may exist as the aberrant offspring of kindred parents, he preferred the latter; nor did he think that reason or religion would be shocked if science should hereafter declare it probable, that the earliest human beings were not called into existence out of nothing, or directly from the dust of the earth, but were children of Simiae nearest in structure to men,* and were made, by some influence of variation, to differ from their progenitors in having a brain and general structure such, and so formed, that the breath of immortal life could be breathed into them, and distinguish them forever from the animals from whom and above whom they had risen.

---

* Although Darwin in his *Origin of Species* refrained from directly applying his theory to man, very few readers missed the obvious implication. The ancestry of man, in fact, was in many cases taken to be the main issue.

CHAPTER 2 — The Threat to the Religious View of Life

Every conventional religious spokesman who mentioned the *Origin* during the first few years condemned it as either being atheistic or conducing in some way to atheism. Most religious writers, however, were not inclined to worry about it a great deal at first, for they considered the theory an unsubstantiated hypothesis which the great Agassiz had rejected as so much rubbish. They felt that there was no reason to be particularly disturbed about the theory until it was scientifically accepted and, of course, they had the assurance of Agassiz and others that this could never happen. A great many other evolutionary theories had appeared in the past, had their brief day, and vanished into the limbo of discarded hypotheses. For the most part, therefore, the earliest religious expressions simply repeated the same arguments, briefly denounced the theory, pointed out that it was entirely unsubstantiated, and expressed the author's lack of perturbation. Ridicule was a favorite technique of debate. A good example of this technique are the following lines of doggerel which were printed in a collection of such verse by *The Methodist* for October 10, 1874.

> And Darwin too, who leads the throng "in vulgam voces
>   spargere,"
> Maintains Humanity is naught except a big menagerie,

> The progeny of tailless apes, sharp eared but Puggy-
>   nosed, Sir,
> Who nightly climbed their "family trees," and on the
>   top reposed, Sir.

Speakers who professed their belief in evolution would often
be asked to prove it by making a man out of a monkey; others
would be asked if they wanted to have apes in their family
tree. The keynote for quite a long time was this kind of
irrelevant heckling, indicative of a general unwillingness to
take the theory seriously.

One man who saw from the beginning that Darwinism posed
a special kind of problem that was not to be overcome by
either distortion or ridicule was the Reverend Joseph P.
Thompson (1819–1879), a Congregational minister of New
York City. As the selection from Thompson clearly indicates,
the real issue had little to do with one way versus another of
making a man. Instead, it focused upon the extent of the
operation of natural law. The operations of Providence had
been circumscribed a bit more tightly by every important
scientific advance since the time of Copernicus. Now, Darwin
by bringing all of organic nature under the operation of the
same set of causal laws, independent of the whim of any Deity,
had apparently written the final chapter in the removal of God
from nature.

REV. JOSEPH P. THOMPSON
Does Science Tend to Materialism? *New Englander, XIX, 1861,*
pp. 85–91

The habit of tracing physical phenomena to discoverable
laws, which belongs to the inductive sciences, may lead the
mind to rest in these as *causal powers,* instead of regarding
them as *formal rules* or modes of operation established by
some higher invisible power. There is a fascination in reducing
a wide range of physical phenomena to a simple law which

defines and governs their relations. Indeed, a great orator has affirmed that the very luxury of such a discovery is a sufficient reward for the toil of the discoverer. . . .

* * *

Now, this very fascination of the discovery of physical laws tends to invest those laws themselves with the reality of living powers. In its exhilaration at having found a proximate reason for a perplexing fact, the mind fancies that it has discovered the original and efficient cause of that fact. And since in every department of nature we can trace many laws of exquisite precision, beauty, and simplicity, there is a strong temptation to regard these formal reasons for phenomena as the original causes of these phenomena. A mind much occupied in tracing particular laws, unless well trained in synthesis and generalization, is liable to rest in the particular law as the end of its inquiry. Instead of pressing on from point to point, with Newton's "why not" and why not? — "if the apple falls, why should not the moon, the planets, the satellites, fall?" — such a mind rests in the simple discovery of the law of accelerated motion by which the apple falls. The facility of tracing particular laws leads some scientists to conceive of the universe as a mere system of self-evolving laws. Thus Darwin closes his essay on "the origin of species by natural selection," by grouping together various forms of life as the evolution of a few general laws, . . .

* * *

This doctrine that the whole universe of matter and of life is a self-evolving system of laws, is really a materialistic pantheism. True, Darwin speaks of "the plan of creation," and "the laws impressed on matter by the Creator"; and his theory of development through the evolution of organic laws is not necessarily inconsistent with belief in a personal God. . . . But the fascination of the idea of progressive evolution by physical laws, leads Darwin to conceive of the Creator as filling some

honorary office rather than as performing any efficient function in the universe. Thus, in treating of the structure of the
eye, he says, "It is scarcely possible to avoid comparing the
eye to a telescope. We know that this instrument has been
perfected by the long-continued efforts of the highest human
intellect; and we naturally infer that the eye has been formed
by a somewhat analogous process. But may not this inference
be presumptuous? Have we any right to assume *that the
Creator works by intellectual powers like those of man?*" He
then supposes the formation of this delicate complex organ to
be the result of "transitional grades," the process steadily
advancing through "numerous, successive, slight, modifications." "In living bodies," he argues, "variation will cause the
slight alterations, generation will multiply them almost infinitely, and natural selection will pick out with unerring skill
each improvement. Let this process go on for millions on
millions of years; and during each year in millions of individuals of many kinds; and may we not believe that a living
optical instrument might thus be formed as superior to one of
glass, as the works of the Creator are to those of man?" This
reference to the Creator seems a complimentary allusion rather
than a necessity of the author's logic, since the theory really
denies to the Creator any personal superintendence of his
works or any direct agency in producing them; while it per-
sonifies the laws of nature as intelligent powers. Indeed, . . . it
goes to the extent of endowing Nature with creative self-
activity. Darwin puts this in so many words, when he says
that "Natural Selection is daily and hourly scrutinizing,
throughout the world, every variation, even the slightest;
rejecting that which is bad, preserving and adding up all that
is good; silently and insensibly working, whenever and wherever opportunity offers, at the improvement of each organic
being, in relation to its organic and inorganic conditions of
life." What then is the Creator but an Emersonian Fate: "Let
us build altars," chants the high priest of Pantheism, "to the
Beautiful Necessity, which secures that all is made of one

piece. . . ." [Emerson, Conduct of Life, p. 42.] And what is this again but the transcendent negation of the Hegelian philosophy, that pure and undetermined existence is pure Nothing. The personality of God vanishes before such a personification of Law. . . .

This transformation of phenomenal *laws* into self-evolving *powers* is certainly an abuse of the inductive principle. The sphere of phenomenal laws is too narrow for the interpretation of the whole order of Nature. It is as if the mechanical philosopher, arguing from the perfect adaptations and wonderful results of certain mechanical forces, should maintain that the universe is made up of such forces; whereas chemical affinity is a law or force of a higher order than the mechanical, and sometimes includes this; and then the chemist should say: "*I* have discovered the original and highest principles of nature, in the chemical forces of my laboratory;" but vital powers are of a higher order than either mechanical or chemical forces, and include them both; and then the physiologist should say: "*I* have discovered the essential life of nature in these vital powers:" — and yet, what physiologist has given a "precise, tenable, and consistent" definition of *life?* And when we pass into Biology, and begin to discuss the soul as an animating principle or essence, we are already within the confines of that spiritual and invisible world, where we must admit the action of powers that our senses cannot measure. But to rest in particular laws is to rest upon the surface of things; or at least to carry our dissection of nature no deeper than the cuticle. And a materialistic philosophy is only superficial. As Bacon has said: "a little natural philosophy inclines men to atheism; but depth in philosophy always brings them about to religion. For while the mind looks upon second causes scattered, it may sometimes go no further; but when it beholds the chain of them collected and linked together, it must needs have recourse to Providence and a Deity."

To rest in ascertained physical laws as *first* causes, is much as if an inventor should become so enamored of the working

of his own machine, as to rate it above the mind that had
invented it; and should worship the product of his own hands
as a creating force. Whereas the true logic of the machine
is — if this adaptation of mechanical powers is so wonderful,
how much more wonderful the mind that discovered or
conceived it, and how infinitely greater than both the Author
of that mind and of the physical forces which its ingenuity
has brought together in the machine. Having admired first
the crude forces and materials of nature, and next these as
combined by invention, and then the genius of the inventor,
can we stop short of the great thought of God? In the Patent
Office one is continually reminded of the supremacy of the
human intelligence over inert matter. Now, the universe is
the "patent office" of the Creator, from whose material combinations He can no more be precluded than perpetual motion
can be invented or evolved from mechanical forces.

The physical universe is a storehouse of immeasurable treas-
ures, shut up under a combination-lock; particular sciences are
the prongs of the key which man adjusts to various tumblers,
until he spells out the magic word and opens the lock. How
childish, how absurd, to claim that these sciences, or the laws
which they combine into a system, made the lock, and stored
the treasury! Yet such is the logic of materialism; and that
result is possible only to minds that move in the tread-mill of
physical laws, till they imagine these to be the final seat and
source of power. . . .

CHAPTER 3

The Scientific Rejection of Darwinism

To students of the present day, the theory of evolution by natural selection seems almost axiomatic. It is often difficult to imagine a time when evolution was not accepted, and it is difficult to attain any kind of sympathetic understanding of the point of view of theological opponents. As so often happens after a new theory has become established, those who had initially opposed it are now seen as obscurantists or old fogies who struck out willfully against "the Truth."

Nevertheless, the most significant of the arguments against Darwinism were not theological; they were arguments advanced by scientists who were disturbed either by the incomplete agreement of the theory with the facts they were familiar with, or by Darwin's evident use of a hypothetical mode of reasoning. Darwin's argument was not perfect — there were many gaps of which he was painfully aware, and the paleontological, embryological, and other evidence that was to confirm the theory and secure for it the near unanimity of support which it now enjoys accumulated gradually. In addition to these gaps, which were bridged eventually by Darwin's supporters as they attempted to meet the objections of critics, there were some matters about which Darwin was simply, and demonstrably, wrong. In these cases the error was so intertwined with what was correct that many critics were moved to dismiss the *Origin in toto*. We now know, for example, that he was totally wrong in his remarks upon how heredity occurs, that he ascribed far too much active power to the environment, and, even more seriously, we know that the variation upon which evolution is based is not minute and continuous as Darwin supposed, but it is discrete and discontinuous. Contrary to Darwin, nature does, indeed, make leaps, and these leaps, or mutations, are the raw materials of evolution.

Darwinism best illustrates how a significant innovation in one branch of science is dependent upon — or perhaps influences — changes in other areas often quite remote. It also illustrates that a workable scientific theory that offers advantages not possessed by older theories can be accepted even if it is incomplete. Scientists who have accepted the theory will simply use it where it applies and hope that the anomalies will be removed by further research.

Some of the anomalies are, in fact, still being debated. A whole class of characteristics which had no apparent survival value — in fact, in many cases they seemed to have negative survival value — were explained by Darwin in terms of his concept of "sexual selection." These included the brighter plumage of male birds of many species, the unwieldy — although beautiful — antlers on some deer, and a whole variety of similar characteristics which seemed to function only as attractions in courtship and to be dysfunctional in every other consideration. Again, in certain populations, there exist classes of sterile male workers who have what appear to be regular socially assigned functions useful only to other members of the community. When challenged to show how such traits could result from natural selection, Darwin replied that this was a case of "group selection," a process that seemed to work independently of natural selection. In neither of these cases have satisfactory answers yet been provided; scientists still debate the range of sexual selection and the reality of group selection.

In the early years of the theory, one could have added a great many more apparently destructive arguments. On the theory of heredity then current, for example, one could "prove" that Darwin's version of evolution was impossible, for it was easy to show that unless new characters appeared in an inconceivably large number of individuals at the same time, they would be swamped by the old characters. This difficulty was not removed until long after acceptance of evolution.* Until that time, biologists had to content themselves with pointing out "the depths of our ignorance" on the subject of heredity, but this particular ignorance remained a potent source of embarrassment for them. Again, physicists had demonstrated, according to the best methods available to them, that the sun could not have existed long enough for Darwin's method to work; physicists and biologists were therefore working in separate worlds until a better method of estimating the sun's age was developed — once again, long after the acceptance of evolution.

Given all these difficulties and unanswered questions, it was only to be expected that during the early years Darwin would have some powerful opponents within the scientific camp. A great many of these scientists, to be sure, never revealed any evidence of having a clear understanding of Darwin's particular theory, contenting themselves instead with general objections to "development hypotheses"; others demanded too much of the new theory, insisting that it be absolutely proven before it be given a hearing; still others used the familiar argument of distortion and innuendo. Yet, when all this is granted, it remains true that the best of the opponents' arguments were reasonable and, in terms of the knowledge of the time, perhaps

---

* One of the most important discoveries of Mendel was that inheritance was always in terms of unit characters which do not blend, and that a characteristic which does not show up in one generation may appear unaltered in the next. The swamping of any character by another is therefore impossible. Mendel's laws, however, were not incorporated into science until the turn of the century.

as good as those arguments in support of the theory. Later generations are too often disposed to believe that those who turned out to be on the "wrong side" of a scientific dispute were overly conservative. Most scientists, on the contrary, reacted as scientists should when faced with a new hypothesis carrying such profound consequences for a whole world view — cautiously and critically. The positive effect of their criticism was the stimulation of a vast body of research designed to fill in gaps in the theory and remove the difficulties which they pointed out. Historically, such stimulation of research has been a primary function of the scientific critic, who thereby earns an important place in any account of "scientific progress."

The scientific critics are represented by William North Rice, whose 1867 doctoral dissertation, written under the direction of James Dwight Dana of Yale, meticulously examined and rejected Darwin's theory.

Rice's argument included a critique of all those points which Gray recognized as weak elements of the theory, but he also made a great deal of the apparent inability of Darwinism to account for anything really new. Darwin's natural selection, he granted, could improve any existing characteristic, but he did not see how it could explain the origin of novelty — say, the first appearance of an instinct, or the beginning of an optic nerve. Recalling that Darwin did not recognize the evolutionary significance of "sports" or "mutations" Rice's argument carries weight, for minute variations of a character that does not exist is difficult to conceive of. Darwin's excessive gradualism, in other words, represented by his adoption of the medieval axiom that "nature does not make leaps," provided an insuperable difficulty for the theory in its original form. It was not until the turn of the century, with the work of Hugo de Vries, that this difficulty was overcome by the recognition that the "leaps" of nature were really the most significant variations. It should be noted, however, that Rice, who shortly changed his mind about evolution, gave a great deal of weight to what he termed the "antecedent probability" of a naturalistic hypothesis as opposed to a supernaturalistic one.

Another class of scientifically-oriented critics focused not so much on particular instances that contradicted the theory as they did upon Darwin's methodology, for Darwin's work differed in many ways from the generally accepted view of the inductive process, in which one was thought to collect the "facts," with no preconceived notions about them, add them up in some way, and allow an "explanation" to grow naturally out of the facts. Instead, Darwin presented to the world one of the first examples of the long, tightly reasoned hypothetical method that has come to be characteristic of modern science. The *Origin* is, in reality, one long interwoven argument. Assuming that such-and-such was the case, Darwin said time after time, we can account for such and such appearances.

Many who had been schooled in an earlier version of scientific method recoiled at Darwin's violation of it. Thus, J. Lawrence Smith, president of the American Association for the Advancement of Science and a distinguished scientist of the old school, regretted Darwin's "highly wrought imagination" and considered him more of a metaphysician than a scientist.

The other critiques are included to show how certain points of Darwin's methodology, or the apparent implications of his work for science, were seized upon by older philosophers or specialists in the logic of science. D. R. Goodwin, for example, the newly-appointed Provost of the University of Pennsylvania, was concerned by the doctrine of chance which he thought was implied by Darwin's version of evolution. The article by Francis Bowen is an outstanding example of the most common type of argument used by philosophers who were themselves not practicing scientists. Mid-nineteenth century philosophers were trained in formal logic and were always on the lookout for fallacious thinking. Since they did not possess the specialized knowledge increasingly required for evaluating the scientists' facts, logical consistency was perhaps the only tool that the highly educated non-scientist could use to test the evidence presented by scientists. Although he himself was guilty of a certain amount of fallacious thinking, Bowen clearly shows that Darwin's book did not measure up to a logician's standards. Neither, of course, would any other important empirical hypothesis, for one of the things we have learned since the time of Darwin is that empirical science and logic are two different things. To test such an hypothesis as that of natural selection, one must appeal, not to logic, but to what is, in fact, the case in nature. In the long run, this discovery may have been the most important philosophical implication of Darwin's book.

WILLIAM   NORTH   RICE
Darwinian Theory of the Origin of Species, *New Englander, 1867, pp. 607–633*

It is much to be regretted that the discussion of this question has often assumed a character rather theological than scientific. The pulpit and the religious press have generally been far more ready to denounce the Darwinian theory as materialistic and atheistic, than to consider the scientific evidences on which it rests. . . . The course of these theologians is as prejudicial to the interests of religion, as it is contrary to the spirit of science. It is no service to a good cause to teach men that the truth of Christianity is dependent on the decision of a still doubtful question in science. The whole history of philosophy, — the shameful retreat of the church from point to point, after each vain endeavor to check the progress of science, — the noble minds who after each scientific discovery have been led to reject the faith which its recognized expounders had founded on scientific error — driven into infidelity, not by the supposed infidel tendencies of science, but by the folly of Christian teachers — ought long ago to have taught the lesson which the church seems still so slow to learn. For the sake of religion as well as science, let scientific questions be discussed and settled on purely scientific grounds. . . .

*   *   *

The great strength of the Darwinian theory, as of any theory of development, lies in its coincidence with the general spirit and tendency of science. It is the aim of science to narrow the domain of the supernatural, by bringing all phenomena within the scope of natural laws and secondary causes. . . . Things which seem most irregular and capricious — the course of the winds, the arrangement of foliage, the forms of continents, the position of mountains, plains, lakes, and deserts — are seen to be determined by laws as changeless as those which fix the orbits of the planets. This tendency of science is sometimes condemned as atheistical, but it is perfectly consistent with the purest theism. For God works in nature no less than in the supernatural. The difference which we recognize between the two, is merely subjective. Any effect of Divine power which can be embraced in the formulas of science, we call natural; those which cannot be thus formulated, we call supernatural or miraculous. As every chain of secondary causes must have a beginning in the fiat of the First Cause, there must be a limit at which the natural passes into the supernatural. At this point science must terminate. But this limit is to be determined by scientific investigation, not prescribed by philosophic dogmatism. Science has repeatedly passed the supposed boundaries of possible discovery. Whether, in any particular direction, the real limit of scientific progress is already reached, or infinitely remote, no one can a priori determine. But the latter must always be assumed till the former is proved. Thus, in the case before us, it may be that we shall be compelled to admit half a million distinct miracles to account for the phenomena of organic nature, but it is clearly the duty of science to seek for some other explanation. . . .

*   *   *

Before passing from these general views to a more special examination of the evidence, it is necessary to settle precisely what must be proved in order to entitle the hypothesis in question [Darwinism] to our acceptance. It is often said that the burden of proof must devolve upon the new theory, and many people seem to imagine that a new theory requires for its support a kind and degree of evidence entirely different from that which would suffice in the case of an old theory. This spirit of conservatism, while it is exceedingly useful in practical matters, should have little weight in purely theoretical investigations. The truth of a doctrine depends not on its age: novelty is no synonym for error, or even for improbability. It is commonly said that it will be time to believe in Darwinism when we see an ape turning into a man; and even so able a thinker as Agassiz has condescended to argue in a manner somewhat similar. But historical proof is not to be required in hypothetical reasoning. The questions by which an hypothesis is to be tried, are these: — Is the cause assigned for the phenomena a *vera causa?** Is it competent to produce in kind and degree the effects required? Can the phenomena be accounted for as well by any other hypothesis?

That the principle of Natural Selection really exists in nature, and has been largely efficient in the production of varieties and geographical races, none can doubt. The third question is as easily answered as the first. The only alternative is the admission of half a million of miracles, and in science the supernatural is to be admitted only when all naturalistic hypotheses fail. The theory, then, must stand or fall in accordance with the answer which may be given to the second question. Is natural selection competent to produce in kind and degree the actual phenomena of organic existence? If the facts are precisely and only such as this principle would ac-

---

* *Vera causa*, in the nineteenth century, was generally understood to imply an agent whose existence could be demonstrated independently of the phenomena it was supposed to explain and which could also be proven adequate for the production of the phenomena in question.

count for, we must fully adopt the theory. If some phenomena exist which the principle does not perfectly account for, or some phenomena are unknown which according to the theory we should expect to find, we must receive it with doubt and suspicion. If we find any class of phenomena positively contrary to the theory, the theory must be rejected. . . .

*   *   *

The main position of the Darwinians, in its most general statement, is, that the morphological, teleological, chronological, and geographical relations of all organic beings are precisely what might have resulted from such a course of variation as is supposed.

It is to be remarked, however, that these relations are also precisely what might have resulted from special creation. Admitting for the present that nothing in organic nature is inconsistent with the hypothesis of development, it is certain that there is nothing inconsistent with the hypothesis of direct creation by a wise and benevolent Deity; — a Deity working out designs infinite and perfect through the medium of finite and imperfect matter; . . . This would seem sufficiently obvious; yet, as the fact has been sometimes overlooked, and sometimes expressly denied by the Darwinians, it may be worth while to consider it more at length. . . .

*   *   *

From the facts and arguments thus far considered, it would appear that the phenomena of organic nature are equally well accounted for on the theories of transmutation and special creation; but that, in the absence of other evidence, the theory of transmutation should be preferred, as being naturalistic, while the other is supernaturalistic. There are, however, important facts in nature which, it is claimed, are contrary to the Darwinian theory. It remains for us, then, to examine the objections to Darwinism.

The most obvious objection is that which is drawn from the general permanence of known species within the period of human history. Varieties have indeed sprung up under domestication, but in these cases the animals or plants have been placed under conditions very different from those which exist in nature, and the breeds or races thus produced seem gradually to lose their peculiarities when removed from artificial conditions. Among wild species variations occur; but these seem oscillatory, rather than progressive, and introduce no change in the specific type. The descriptions of our best known species given by the most ancient naturalists are as applicable now as then. The figures of animals which have come down to us among the fragments of ancient art, are sufficiently accurate representations of the species with which we are most familiar to-day. And the strength of this argument is greatly increased by the fact that some of our present species can be traced back geologically to a period long preceding the commencement of recorded history. . . . Such facts as these constitute an argument of some force against the theory, but are by no means conclusive. The period of recorded history is too short to be appreciable in the progress of organized nature. And the mere fact of certain species remaining essentially permanent for immense periods proves nothing decisively, for the Darwinian theory involves no rapid or constant change in specific types. On the contrary, Darwin expressly says that "natural selection always acts very slowly, generally at only long intervals of time, and generally on only a very few of the inhabitants of the same region at the same time." Again, "The periods during which species have been undergoing modification, though very long as measured by years, have probably been short in comparison with the periods during which these same species remained without undergoing any change."

Another objection is closely connected with the one already considered. If species had arisen by variation, ought we not to find an indefinite number of gradational forms between them?

There are indeed some cases in which the boundaries of species are doubtful; there are some forms whose specific character is admitted and denied by perhaps equally competent authority. But, setting aside those species which have been described from an inadequate number of specimens, or by incompetent or careless writers, the limits of the vast majority of species are exceedingly well defined. Each species is surrounded by a chasm, not always wide, but no less impassable, bridged by no gradational forms. And there are broader gaps separating genera, families, and groups of higher degree. The answer of the Darwinians is, that, as the forms developed by natural selection come into competition with the less improved, the latter must inevitably become extinct. Hence we might expect that the transition from one existing form to another would be oftener by a saltus than by imperceptible gradations.

But this extinction of less favored forms is not precisely simultaneous with the development of improved forms, and is a gradual process which may be in progress during long periods. Hence it would appear that in the older groups the extinction should have been more complete, so that species, genera, and other divisions recognized in systems of classification would be bounded by broad lines of demarcation. On the other hand, it would seem that groups more recently introduced ought to present more difficulty to the systematist, the gradational forms connecting species, genera, &c., not having all become extinct. We have not been able to make a thorough comparison in this respect, and can present no positive conclusions. Yet it is our impression that the result of such a comparison would be unfavorable to the Darwinian theory, the groups more recently introduced generally admitting of more exact definition and classification than those which have come down from more ancient time. . . . Especially striking in this view is the chasm between man and the apes, since the quadrumana date only from the Tertiary, and man seems to have been the last work of creation. Here, if anywhere, we should expect to find a series of closely gradational forms. But this comparison, though made with all possible care and thoroughness, would yield but uncertain results; for, where gradational forms appear between different groups, it would often be impossible to determine whether they are remnants of preexistent forms, or results of incipient processes of variation. . . .

Geology blends these two objections into one, and gives to them a vastly increased force. "Rarity, as geology tells us, is the precursor to extinction." So says Darwin. This is true to a certain extent in regard to more comprehensive groups, but not in regard to species. On the contrary, species generally disappear suddenly. The individuals of each species are as common in the uppermost bed in which they occur, as in the lowest, or any intermediate bed. But species are not only undiminished in numbers as we approach the boundary of their geological range. They are unchanged in character. And when, in the superjacent stratum, we meet with a new species, the transition is not by imperceptible gradations, but by a saltus. . . .

*   *   *

Such facts as these seem almost fatal to the theory of transmutation, but Darwin's answer is far more satisfactory than would seem possible. He justly affirms the geological record to be far less perfect than geologists have usually claimed, though perhaps he somewhat exaggerates its imperfection. Fossiliferous deposits of considerable thickness can be formed only where the sea-bottom is subsiding at a rate nearly equal to that of the deposition of sediment. . . .

*   *   *

Probably in those localities where the series of fossiliferous strata is most complete, less than half of the time past has left any legible records in the rocks. These gaps in the record in different localities can be partly filled up by mutual intercalation, but for this purpose how small a portion of the earth's crust has been with any degree of thoroughness explored! and how much must ever remain inaccessible! Not only have there been vast periods in which no rocks now accessible were formed; many of the strata which exist, are ill adapted for the preservation of fossils, and consequently are almost barren. Of all the myriads of living creatures that have constituted earth's teeming population in the successive geological periods, what an infinitesimal remnant has been preserved! No wonder that we cannot discern the former continuity of the chain of organic life, when so many of its links have rusted away, and so many others are concealed beneath ocean waves or mountain masses. As to how far this reasoning removes the objections which we have cited, different minds will form different opinions. A theory which is forced thus to slink into the darkest corners of uncertainty, must be regarded with considerable suspicion. Yet these objections are not conclusive; and opposed to them is the great a priori plausibility of a naturalistic theory in distinction from a supernaturalistic. Were there no other objectons than these, the theory of Darwin would seem entitled to a somewhat hesitating provisional adoption. . . .

*   *   *

But, though the non-existence of gradational forms between existing or extinct species constitutes no conclusive argument against the theory of transmutation, the case would be quite different if types should be found exhibiting plans of structure radically distinct, so that gradational forms between them would be impossible or inconceivable.

Theoretically, natural selection might make any amount of change in degree. Nascent organs might be developed to any extent. Organs now largely developed might be reduced to rudiments; but no new plan of structure could be established. Strict relations of homology would bind together all organisms, however changed in external form or teleological adaptations. On the contrary, we find in the animal kingdom (disregarding for the present the Protozoa) four distinct plans of structure. . . .

*   *   *

These different types are entirely distinct from each other in their general structure and in the single elements of which they are composed. The spheromere of the Radiate, the sack of the Mollusk, the arthromere of the Articulate, and the vertebra of the Vertebrate can have with each other no homology. All homologies are limited by the boundaries of these sub-kingdoms. And these groups are as radically distinct in embryological development as in the structure of the adult. We must, then, conclude that a direct genetic connection between any two of these groups is impossible.

But some would seek to trace such a connection between the Protozoa and each of these four sub-kingdoms respectively. The Protozoa may be considered as "systemless," and in the lowest of them scarcely any specialization of parts is manifest. It might be argued that in these every part is virtually homologous with every other, so that the process of specialization might take a direction towards either of the systems of structure indifferently. The question would then arise, "how could the first steps in advancement or in the differentiation and specialization of parts have been taken?"

Darwin modestly declines to answer, declaring that, "as we have no facts to guide us, all speculation on the subject is useless." . . .

*   *   *

But, passing this question, and admitting that in some way a transition might be effected from systemless Protozoa to low forms of Radiates, Mollusks, and Articulates, we have still the world-wide chasm between the Protozoan and the Fish to be bridged simply by imagination or by faith. Some naturalists have discovered in the Protozoa resemblances to the three lower specialized types, and have classified them accordingly as Actinozooids, Malacozooids, and Entomozooids; but no one has discovered in any of the Protozoa any approximation to the vertebrate type. This gap is rendered yet more vast by the consideration that the earliest known fishes are not hypotypic, but even hypertypic, exhibiting some characters of higher classes. These first ganoids and selachians bear a testimony in favor of special creation, which, in the present state of science, no facts contradict, and no argument can set aside.

And it is not merely one isolated instance of special creation which is thus established. The admission of a plurality of distinct creations, to which we are thus forced, breaks down that universal analogy on which, more than on any matters of facts, the Darwinian theory depends. In the claim that all life, or even all animal life, is one by lineal descent from a common ancestor, there is much philosophic plausibility; but, if a plurality of original forms must be admitted, it makes little difference how many of them are supposed.

Natural selection can originate no new function. Admitting that variation may advance a function already existing to any degree whatever, or localize in some special organ a function previously exerted by the whole organism indifferently, or obliterate by disuse a function no longer useful, yet the origination of a new function can only be ascribed to direct creation.

If, then, all animals are descended from a common ancestor, no function can exist which did not exist in the simple forms with which life is supposed to have commenced. But is this true? In the complex chemistry by which food is elaborated into all the varied structures which compose a highly organized animal body — in the production of the secretions, venomous or otherwise, which are peculiar to certain species or groups, — in the electricity of certain fishes, and the phosphorescence of certain insects, — in the subtle mysteries of viviparous reproduction, — in the mammalian habit of nourishing their young, — in special sensation executed by organs of such complication as the eye and ear in the higher animals or in man, — is there no function which is not possessed by beings whose bodies are but sarcode, whose blood is scarcely more than seawater, whose eggs form no germinal vesicle, and whose highest manifestation of life consists in enveloping in their gelatinous mass some smaller infusoria with which chance may bring them into contact?

But, passing this question, it is to be noticed that the same principle must hold good in regard to mental faculties. Not that thought is merely a function of the bodily organism. No notion could be more false or more pernicious. We are taught that in another state of existence the human mind, though disembodied, is to exercise its faculties in greater perfection than at present. . . . Yet it is no less true that in this state of existence mental action, whether in brute or man, is conditioned on physical organization. The mind of Newton would have manifested nothing above idiocy, had his nervous system been constituted in a manner slightly different.

Considering mental action as thus conditioned on physical organization, it appears that variation and natural selection can develop to any extent a faculty which already exists, but can originate no new faculty. Hence, if all animals have been developed from some simple form, even man can have no faculties which did not exist in that original simple form. In the mental qualities which make the glory of the poet, the philosopher, or the saint, we see only the further development of those powers which exist, in a somewhat rudimentary condition, not merely in gorilla and chimpanzee, but in Amoeba and Eozoon. Probably this doctrine will find few adherents, but it seems a legitimate corollary of the Darwinian theory.

But the theory is as incompetent to explain the instincts of brutes as the higher intelligence of man. It is often difficult to draw the line between instinct and true intelligence, since the two are so frequently blended. Some of the higher animals exhibit marks of reason, while man acts sometimes from instinct. A creature is said to be guided by instinct when it performs any act, whether simple or complex, independently of experience or instruction, and without understanding the purpose which that act is to serve. It is evident that a new instinct is in the strictest sense a new faculty. One instinct cannot be developed into another. The intelligence which in the child builds a cob-house, may, in the man, build a cathedral. But the instinct which in the wasp makes cells of paper, is entirely distinct from that which in the bee makes cells of wax. Hence, natural selection can never account for the origination of a new instinct. Darwin's chapter on instinct is wonderful for its ingenuity, but it is far from being satisfactory. To show that several species have instincts somewhat similar, is a very different thing from showing that any one of these instincts might be derived by inheritance from a species which had no such instinct. . . . Darwin has attempted to show that the instinct which makes the rude wax-cells of the humble-bee, might be developed into the instinct which forms the perfect cells of the hive-bee. The real difficulty in the case would have been more nearly met, if he had told us how the humble-bee inherited its coarse and clumsy instinct from an insect which made no wax-cells at all. One or two examples of simple instincts will further illustrate the point. How could natural selection teach an insect to provide for the larvae of whose existence it could have no knowledge, by laying its eggs in the midst of food suited for its larvae, though entirely different from that used by the perfect insect? How could natural selection teach the mammalian infant the use of the maternal mammae? How could natural selection originate the sexual instinct, when the primal monad had become so far differentiated as to give rise to animals with separated sexes? . . .

* * *

The most decisive argument against the doctrine of Transmutation, is that which is drawn from the phenomena of Hybridism. It appears to be a general law that, within the same species, a union between individuals, as diverse as possible, is most favorable to fertility. Darwin is inclined to believe that even self-impregnating hermaphrodites require at least an occasional cross to keep up the vigor of the species. . . . When different species are crossed, the result is directly the contrary. In most cases the result is no issue whatever.

And in all cases the hybrid offspring are incapable of permanent fertilization inter se. The Darwinians deny that this sterility is quite universal; and, in default of any accepted criterion of specific identity or diversity, there is no means of proving that it is so. Nor is that a matter of any great importance. That there is a general tendency towards a sterility more or less nearly complete, none can deny or question. Here, then, we have the law that divergence of character, within the limits of a specific type, tends to increase fertility, but beyond this limit tends as surely to diminish fertility or to produce absolute sterility.

In the face of these facts, is it not absurd to claim that varieties and species differ only in degree? Are we not forced to the conclusion that there is between them a radical difference in nature and in origin?

The facts of geographical distribution have somewhat of a bearing on our subject, though yielding no positive conclusions on either side. The very wide and interrupted range of many genera is a serious objection to the Darwinian theory. On the theory of special creation, the existence of closely allied or representative species in regions widely distant and separated by impassable barriers, presents no difficulty, as they seem manifestly designed to fill quite similar places in the polity of these different regions. But the attempt to account for their existence and distribution by descent from a common ancestor and migration from a common center, is beset with apparently insuperable difficulties. Darwin's great resource is the supposition of a universal glacial period. It may be questioned whether the facts thus far observed prove anything more than local glacial periods, which may or may not have been contemporaneous. But admitting such a glacial period as Darwin supposes, the case is hardly improved. The idea of tropical species surviving a reduction of climate which enabled temperate species to migrate across the equator, is by no means easy to be received. . . .

* * *

We have already referred to the argument in favor of the Darwinian theory drawn from the succession of similar forms in the same area. The theory meets a corresponding difficulty in the fact that sometimes the fauna or flora of one region at one geological period finds its nearest allies in a subsequent period in some distant region. Such a case is found in the marked analogy between the Miocene flora of Central Europe and the existing flora of Eastern America. . . .

*　*　*

This examination of the Darwinian theory, though too long for the patience of the reader, has been too brief to develop fully the important points of the argument. We have seen that the theory accounts for many of the phenomena of organic nature, and that it has in its favor the antecedent probability which belongs to a naturalistic theory in distinction from a supernaturalistic. On the other hand, we have seen that it encounters many difficulties, that there are many phenomena which it is not competent satisfactorily to explain, and that two important facts — the limitation of homologies and the sterility of hybrids — are directly contrary to it.

In accordance with the rules laid down at the commencement of this discussion, it must therefore be rejected as inconsistent with the present teachings of science. What new facts further investigation may bring to light, or what new relations old facts may be made to assume, time alone can show. Yet it does not seem likely that the aspect of the question will be materially changed. What new theories further thought may devise, none can foretell; yet it would be difficult to conceive of a theory of development which should combine more elements of strength than that which we have considered. The objections to the Darwinian theory are objections to the theory of development in general. The only alternative is the doctrine of special creation. . . .

*　*　*

The rejection of the doctrines of spontaneous generation and transmutation of species will thus bring us to a purely supernaturalistic theory of organic nature. Life is not a property or modification of matter. It is a direct creation by Omnipotence. Here, then, will be found one of those limits of scientific discovery, which, as we have seen, must bound our progress in every direction, though we cannot even conjecture their situation till we have actually reached, and vainly endeavored to pass them. . . .

* * *

Such will probably be the result of the controversy on the most important question now agitating the scientific world. Yet we have used the future tense designedly, for we believe the time has not yet come when the question can be authoritatively and finally decided. On a subject so complex, and so imperfectly studied in many of its bearings, we must be content to hold and teach provisionally those views which seem to us the nearest approximation to the truth, ready to abandon tomorrow every article of the creed we advocate to-day, leaving perhaps to future generations to confirm or to contradict our teachings, and cheerfully accepting as our mission the task of opening, through the gloom of uncertainty, or it may be through the deeper darkness of error, a path for our successors to the perfect truth. . . .

D. R. GOODWIN
Darwin on the Origin of Species, *American Theological Review*, *II, May 1860, pp. 330–344*

The Lamarckian or development theory, as ingeniously set forth in the "Vestiges of the Natural History of Creation," took *law* as its basis and watchword. Under cover of immanent, universal and eternal law, it professed to retain, while in fact it dispensed with, the idea of God as a Creator. But this theory of Mr. Darwin openly dispenses with law itself, it

expressly refuses to recognize any necessary or determinate
law of development or variation; and throws itself without
reserve upon the illimitable ocean of accident. It may be regarded as a most singular revamping in modern form and
phrase, of the old speculation of Leucippus and Democritus,
that all the beautiful and complicated arrangements of the
Kosmos are only the result of a fortuitous concurrence of
atoms. To this theory Darwin simply adds what he calls the
principle of "natural selection," to guide this blind chaotic
struggle of the elements to the well-ordered result. But, after
all, it does not appear that this principle adds any thing to the
scheme except a new name. This natural selection implies no
intention, no intelligent purpose, no rational choice; it is only
another name for the fact, for the result for which it professes
to account. It suggests no real cause. It is in truth no principle
at all. The result itself is represented as the result not of any
antecedently impressed or inherent law, but merely of the play
of circumstances, of the whirl of accident, of the universal
conflict and struggle out of which all forms arise, and in which
they are preserved or destroyed by virtue of their mutual adaptations or antagonisms. . . .

*   *   *

If, with our knowledge of the solar system and of the stellar
universe, we were to express, as we very naturally might, our
incredulity at such a theory, we might be reminded that however vast the distance between the premises and the conclusion, between the assumed conditions and the actual result of
this problem, there have been boundless ages for the process to
go forward in, and no one can tell what immense changes and
modifications might take place in the revolving cycles of a
past eternity. Give us time enough, it might be said, and any
thing may be made out of any thing, or made into any thing;
light may be made out of darkness, order out of chaos, con-
science out of a cucumber, mind out of matter, a sun out of a
handful of mud, an eye out of a fibre of muscle or a bit of skin,

and a man out of a tadpole or a bramble-bush, or all alike from
some common original form; and then changes might go on by
such infinitesimal gradations that they should be absolutely
imperceptible in amount even for tens of thousands of years.
When all impassable distinctions of *kind* are abolished, and
only differences of *degree* remain, time enough will meet all
exigencies and make any hypothesis credible. For, if we should
object that we can see no signs of this process within the limits
of actual experience, or even in the realms of the past, so far
as they are revealed to our inspection, we might be reminded
that our experience is very narrow in its range, and our widest
observation very limited, fragmentary, and imperfect. We
might be told that nevertheless our limited sphere of vision
furnishes us with more confirmations of this scheme than we
had any right to expect; and we might be pointed to the
perturbations that still exist among the heavenly bodies, to
the changes that are still going on upon their surfaces, to the
nebulosities that are still visible here and there in space, and to
the varieties that are still developed among pigeons, pigs, and
sundry plants. The problem might be stated thus: Take the
difference between the rock-pigeon and the tumbler, and call
it *a;* take the time which has been required to evolve this difference, and call it *b;* then take the difference between a man,
with all his high organization, all his intellectual and moral
faculties, and a bat, or a craw-fish, or a blade of timothy, or
a lump of bog-iron ore, or any thing else you please, and call
that difference what you please, any thing short of infinite,
say m^n; and the formula for the time in which it would be
conceivable that this difference should develop itself would be
easily found. It would be $x = bm^n$, a period of time which
would be finite, since all the terms in which it is expressed are
finite. Would not this be a magnificent illustration of the
Baconian method, of Positive science, in short, of reasoning
from the known to the unknown?

Mr. Darwin admits that if there is any arrangement, feature,
form, or flower in the animal or vegetable kingdom "intended
for beauty in the eye of man, or for mere variety," it is fatal

to his theory. This admission goes deeper than he imagines; for, not to say that, in fact, any idea whatever of design or intelligence in the processes of nature is fatal to his theory, it is manifest that not only any development intended for beauty in the eye of man, but any development intended for beauty at all in any degree whatever, is fatal to his theory. His theory cannot account for it. Natural Selection will not help him. All that is beautiful to the eye of man or to the apprehension of any higher intelligence in the universe, wherever it be, in whatever province or kingdom of nature, must, in his theory, in so far as it is beautiful, be the result of sheer accident! Credat philosophia positiva! And yet this philosophy shrinks aghast from the mysteries of the Christian faith. It strains out the gnat and swallows the camel.

We have just said that any idea whatever of design or intelligence in the processes of organic nature is fatal to Mr. Darwin's theory. This may seem too sweeping an assertion; but we think it can be thoroughly substantiated. Mr. Darwin scouts the phrases, "plan of creation," "unity of design," etc., as "expressions under which we only hide our ignorance, and think that we give an explanation when we only restate a fact." Yet the actual results of fulness, of variety in unity, of order and gradation are fully admitted by him as facts, while they are traced to the operation of "Natural Selection." We submit that it is really his theory that, professing to account for the fact, only restates it. Or at most it gives us the process, and that a process assumed without satisfactory proof, in the stead and to the exclusion of the intelligent cause. The intelligent cause might indeed be supposed to effectuate its plans and designs by this process; but the process cannot rationally be substituted for the plan, the design, and the intelligence, so as to dispense with them. But unless this personal, creative intelligence is rejected altogether, we can see no reason why it cannot be supposed to effectuate its plans and designs by other methods, by acts of creation, for example, as precisely as by that process of so-called natural selection. All animal instincts, the instincts of the bee and the ant, for instance, which have

usually been considered most striking proofs of creative intelligence, Mr. Darwin regards as the result of mere accident, and
the process of "natural selection." He declares the grouping
of all organic beings and the prodigal variety of nature to be
utterly inexplicable on the theory of creation. Yet the beautiful
order and the harmonious variety of nature cannot be conceived by him as the result of any design operating in any
other way; for, if they were intended, he declares them to be
utterly fatal, not to the idea of creation, but to his own theory. . . .

*   *   *

A great multitude of questions, it seems to us, might be
asked which Mr. Darwin's theory is bound to answer, but
which it cannot satisfy — questions which the theory, or
rather the fact, of creation answers in the most natural manner. For example, why do men have the same number of
fingers on one hand as on the other, and the same number of
toes as fingers, if every thing is determined by use, and nothing
by creative laws of beauty, proportion and harmony? Why is
not human hair sometimes green or blue, or the iris of the eye
white or red? Can any better reason be given than the good
pleasure of Him who made them? Why should men have a
beard and women none? If it is of use to men, why not to
women? And if it would be of use to women, why should
not natural selection have multiplied the few women who
have it? Why are not men eight or ten feet high, and as strong
as elephants; would it not be useful to them? Why are there
no races of winged men, as well as flying squirrels; is it only
for want of the happy accident for natural selection to start
with? It would be *so* convenient! Perhaps we may expect
such developments among the infinite changes and chances of
an eternal future.

If natural selection is the key to the development of organic
beings, whence come the infinite variety and fulness of the
species of such beings, from the countless infusoria to the
mammoth and the elephant, from the humblest and tiniest moss

to the giant trees of California, from the oyster to rational man? Mr. Darwin admits and insists upon the fulness of nature, according to the adage, *Natura non facit saltum.* But is it not a strange kind of *selection*, which results in taking all sorts and sizes, just as if there were no selection at all? And is it not a strange sort of philosophy, which satisfies itself with natural selection as an explanation of the fact, rather than with the good pleasure and infinite intelligence of a wise and benevolent Creator? The truth is, as we have said, "natural selection" can mean nothing as a cause. . . . Alone, natural selection can accomplish nothing and explain nothing. Unless we are to couple it with chance or fate to solve the problems of nature, and be satisfied in these later scientific days with the old solution of Democritus; we may as well rest at once in an all-wise Creator as the real cause of all things, originating, organizing and disposing all according to his good pleasure, and by regular processes or laws; some of which processes and laws we may humbly learn, but which we are never authorized proudly to prescribe; of which we may avail ourselves for our use and comfort, but which we may never turn against the being and agency of Him who established them. "Shall the thing formed say to Him that formed it, why hast Thou made me thus?" This is indeed mere Scripture; and, for aught we know, Mr. Darwin may be ready to dismiss it with a sneer of scientific contempt. But we honestly confess, that, in our judgment, it contains a greater truth, and a profounder scientific principle than Mr. Darwin's book can boast of. We recommend to those who would follow Bacon's philosophic method, to imitate also Bacon's reverent spirit.

J. LAWRENCE SMITH

Address, *American Association for the Advancement of Science, Proceedings, XXII, 1873, pp. 11–15*

It is not my object to criticise [*sic*] the speculations of any one or more of the modern scientists who have carried their investigations into the world of the imagination; in fact, it could not be done in a discourse so limited in time as this, and only intended as a prologue to our present meeting. But in order to illustrate this subject of method more fully I will refer to Darwin, whose name has become synonymous with progressive development and natural selection, which, as we had thought, died out with Lamarck fifty years ago.

In Darwin we have one of those philosophers whose great knowledge of animal and vegetable life is transcended only by his imagination. In fact, he is to be regarded more as a metaphysician with a highly-wrought imagination than as a scientist, although a man having a most wonderful knowledge of the facts of natural history. . . .

*   *   *

Darwin takes up the law of life and runs it into progressive development. In doing this he seems to me to increase the embarrassment which surrounds us on looking into the mysteries of creation. He is not satisfied to leave the laws of life where he finds them, or to pursue their study by logical and inductive reasoning. His method of reasoning will not allow him to remain at rest; he must be moving onward in his unification of the universe. He started with the lower orders of animals, and brought them through their various stages of progressive development until he supposed he had touched the confines of man; he then seems to have recoiled, and hesitated to pass the boundary which separated man from the lower orders of animals; but he saw that all his previous logic was bad if he stopped there, so man was made from the ape (with which no one can find fault, if the descent be legitimate). This stubborn logic pushes him still farther, and he must find some connecting link with that most remarkable property of the human face called expression; so his ingenuity has given us a very curious and readable treatise on that subject. Yet still another step must be taken in this linking together man and the lower order of animals; it is in connection with language;

and before long it is not unreasonable to expect another production from that most wonderful and ingenious intellect on
the connection between the language of man and the brute
creation. . . .

* * *

Is this to be one of the methods of modern science, I would
ask? While in our ignorance and short-sightedness we should
be careful in pronouncing any assumption as possible or impossible, still there is no reason why these terms should have
much or any weight in the study of science; for in the abstract
all things in nature are possible, not from any demonstration,
but simply because no one can assert an impossibility. What
a mass of confusion science would become if we studied its
possibilities! For then every conceivable possibility would be
entitled to equal consideration. . . .

* * *

Are we to introduce into science a kind of purgatory in
which to place undemonstrable speculations, and keep them
there in a state of probation, and say that science cannot dis-
card a theory as false when it cannot be accepted as true?
Science, which is preeminently the pursuit of truth, has but
one course to pursue: it must either accept or reject what may
be thrust upon it.

What I have said is, in my humble opinion, warranted by
the departure Darwin and others have made from true science
in their purely speculative studies; and neither he nor any
other searcher after truth expects to hazard great and startling
opinions without at the same time courting and desiring criticism; yet dissension from his views in no way proves him
wrong — it only shows how his ideas impress the minds of
other men. . . .

* * *

Our own distinguished naturalist and associate, Prof. Agassiz,
reverts to this theory of evolution in the same positive manner,

and with such earnestness and warmth as to call forth severe editorial criticisms, by speaking of it as a "mere mine of assertion," and of "the danger of stretching inferences from a few observations to a wide field," and he is called upon to collect "real observations to disprove the evolution hypothesis." I would here remark, in defence [sic] of my distinguished friend, that scientific investigation will assume a curious phase when its votaries are required to occupy time in looking up facts, and seriously attempting to disprove any and every hypothesis based upon proof, some of it not even rising to the dignity of circumstantial evidence.

I have dwelt longer on this one point than I had intended; but the very popular manner in which in recent years it has been presented to the public mind of all classes of society, and to persons of all ages, warranted a full notice in speaking of the importance of avoiding, as far as possible, undue speculation in connection with our method of scientific investigation. . . .

FRANCIS   BOWEN

Remarks on the Latest Form of the Development Theory, *Memoirs of the American Academy of Arts and Sciences, n.s., VIII, pp. 98–107, communicated March 27, April 10 and May 1, 1860*

[*In the omitted portion of this article, Bowen reduced the Darwinian theory into the five assertions of which he said it consisted. The first two, the fact that individuals vary, and the fact that variations could be inherited, Bowen was ready to grant with only minor reservations. His real criticism begins with the third point.*]

3. But with whatever success the doctrine of Inherited Variation may be applied to explain the existence of Varieties, it is certain that the origin of *Species* can be accounted for on the Development Theory, if at all, only by Cumulative Varia-

tion, — that is, only by supposing a vast number of Inherited Variations to be successively superinduced one upon another. Doubts have been raised upon this point only on account of ambiguity in the meaning of words, or from want of agreement as to the principles of classification. Many races, both of animals and vegetables, appear to be so nearly allied to each other, that certain naturalists consider them as mere Varieties; others persist in considering them as so many distinct Species. Mr. Darwin himself remarks that the distinction between Varieties and Species is "entirely vague and arbitrary"; . . . Fortunately we do not need, so far as our main question is concerned, to enter into the intricacies of this discussion. The advocates of the Development Theory undertake to prove that *all* Species of animals, even those differing most widely from each other, "have descended from at most four or five progenitors, and plants from an equal or lesser number." Putting aside altogether, therefore, the much debated question whether the several races of men are only Varieties, or are so many distinct Species, and the same question with respect to dogs, there is no doubt that men and dogs belong respectively to different Species. And generally, putting aside the question whether the offspring of certain races when crossed are entirely sterile or only partially so, there is no doubt that animals or plants belong to distinct Species when they cannot be crossed or made to interbreed at all. It is enough to say, then, that only Cumulative Variation — and that of a vast number of successive steps — will account for the common origin of animals which will not copulate with each other, or of plants which cannot be crossed.

Now, on this cardinal point, which contains the essence of the Development Theory, since all the other questions involved in it are of no substantive importance, so far as what may be called the Philosophy of Creation is concerned, the direct evidence fails altogether, and we are left exclusively to the guidance of conjecture and analogy and estimates of what is possible for all that we know to the contrary. It is not even pretended that we have any direct proof, either from observation or testimony, that two Species so distinct that they will not interbreed have yet sprung from common ancestors. On the contrary, Mr. Darwin's own supposition is, that the process of developing two entirely distinct Species out of a third is necessarily so gradual and protracted as to require a *quasi* eternity for its completion, so that only a small portion of it could have been accomplished during the limited period of man's existence upon the earth.

In the absence of any direct proof, then, it remains to be inquired if there are sufficient grounds of probability, reasoning from analogy and the principles of inductive logic, for believing that all Species of animals and plants may have originated from three or four progenitors. In speaking of the amount and frequency of Individual Variation, Mr. Darwin and his followers abuse the word *tendency*. After heaping up as many isolated examples of it as they can gather, they assert the legitimate inference from such cases to be, that the Species *tends* to vary, leaving out of view the fact that a vastly larger number of individuals of the same Species do not vary, but conform to the general type. And though only one out of a hundred of these Individual Variations is transmitted by inheritance, yet, after collecting as many instances of such transmission as they can find, they affirm that a Variation *tends* to become hereditable. But it is not so. *Tendency* is rightly inferred only from the *majority* of cases; a small minority of favorable instances merely shows the *tendency* to be the other way. Thus, the cars do not *tend* to run off the track, although one train out of a thousand may be unlucky enough to do so; but the general law is, that they remain on the track. Otherwise, people would not risk their lives in them. . . . The advocates of the Development Theory violate the first principles of inductive logic, by founding their induction not, as they should do, on the majority — the great majority — of cases, but on the exceptions, the accidents. Their whole proceeding is an attempt to establish a philosophy of nature, or a theory of

creation, on anomalies, — on rare accidents, — on *lusus na-*
turae.

This single objection is fatal to Mr. Darwin's theory, which
depends on the accumulation, one upon another, of many successive instances of departure from the primitive type. For if
even Individual Variation appears only in one case out of a
hundred, — and all naturalists will admit this proportion to be
as large as the facts will warrant, — and if, out of the cases in
which it does appear, not more than one in a hundred is perpetuated by inheritance, then should a second Variation happen, what chance has it of leaping upon the back of one of
the former class? The chance is one out of $100 \times 100 \times$
$100 = 1,000,000$. And the chance of a third Variation being
added to a second, which in turn has been cumulated upon a
first, will be one out of 100 raised to the fourth power, or
100,000,000. It is not necessary to carry the computation any
further, especially as Mr. Darwin states that the process of
development can be carried out "only by the preservation and
accumulation of infinitesimally small inherited modifications."
Of course, the interval between two Species so distinct that
they will not interbreed could be bridged over only by a vast
number of modifications thus minute; and on this calculation
of the chances, the time required for the development of *one*
of these Species out of the other would lack no characteristic
of eternity except its name. But the theory requires us to
believe that this process has been repeated an indefinite number
of times, so as to account for the development of *all* the Species
now in being, and of all which have become extinct, out of
four or five primeval forms. If the indications from analogy,
on which the whole speculation is based, are so faint that the
work cannot have been completed except in an infinite lapse of
years, these indications practically amount to nothing. The
evidence which needs to be multiplied by infinity before it will
produce conviction, is no evidence at all.

4. What is here called the "Struggle for Life" is only another name for the familiar fact, that every Species of animal

and vegetable life has its own Conditions of Existence, on which its continuance and its relative numbers depend. Remove any one of these Conditions, and the whole Species must perish; abridge any of them, and the number of individuals in the Species must be lessened. The intrusion of a new race which is more prolific, more powerful, more hardy, or in any way better adapted to the locality, may gradually crowd out some of its predecessors, or restrict them within comparatively narrow bounds. Thus the introduction of the Norway rat has banished the former familiar plague of our households and barns from many of its old haunts, and probably reduced the whole number in this Species to a mere fraction of what it once was. Civilized man also has successfully waged war against many ferocious or noxious animals, and probably exterminated some of them. But the appearance of a rival or hostile race is not the only cause of such diminution or extinction. A change in the physical features of a given district may partially or entirely depopulate it, without the necessary introduction of any new-comers. The drying up or filling up of a lake is necessarily fatal to all its aquatic tribes. The gradual submergence of an island or a continent must exterminate, sooner or later, all the native Species which were peculiar to it. And at the utmost, the failure of any Condition of Existence, whatever may be its character, only leaves vacant ground for the future introduction or creation of new forms of life, without tending in the slightest degree to bring such new forms into existence.

5. Natural Selection, also, as already remarked, has nothing to do with the *origin* of Species, and, in its abstract form, is only the statement of a truism. Of course, when two or more Species crowd each other, the more prolific or the more vigorous, other things being equal, is more likely to gain possession of the disputed ground, and thus to diminish the numbers of the other or oblige it to migrate, or, in rare cases, to kill it out altogether. But this last supposition is a conceivable rather than a probable result. All observation goes to show, that every Species retains a very persistent hold upon life,

however feeble may be the tenure of existence for its individual members. Its numbers may be materially diminished; it may be forced to shift its ground, and to suffer in consequence some slight change in its habits; (Mr. Darwin himself tells us of upland geese and of woodpeckers where there are no trees); it may be driven into holes and corners; but somehow it still survives. Utter extinction of a Species is one of the rarest of all events; not half a dozen cases can be enumerated which are known to have taken place since man's residence upon the earth. And these, surely, are a very insufficient basis on which to found a theory embracing all forms of life. Yet man is the greatest exterminator the world has ever known. His physical powers, coupled with the use of reason by which they are multiplied a thousand-fold, enables him to wage internecine war with comparative ease against nearly every race that molests him. Only the insect tribes, through their immense numbers and their littleness, can successfully defy him; and these not always. In *his* Struggle for Life, all other creatures, animal or vegetable, must retreat or perish. Yet how few has he rooted out altogether! But the Development Theory requires us to believe that this process of extinction, guided by Natural Selection, has been repeated well-nigh to infinity. Not only all the races which are now found only in their stone coffins, but countless others, — "the interminable number of *intermediate* forms which must have existed" as connecting links, and a still greater crowd of other Varieties not intermediate, but gross, rude, and purposeless in their formation, — the unmeaning creations of an unconscious cause, — must all have perished, each through its own peculiar repetition of a series of events so infrequent that we can hardly compute the chances of their happening at all.

It is easy to see why the extermination of a Species, even upon the conditions of Mr. Darwin's theory, should be so infrequent. He holds that all the races which have originated upon the earth since the primeval act of creation first grudgingly threw only four or five seeds of existence into the ground, have been shaded into each other by gradations so slight as to be nearly imperceptible. Differing so slightly from each other, the advantage possessed by any one of them in the Struggle for Life must have been almost indefinitely small. But a peculiarity important enough to preserve those who have it, while whole Species must die out because they have it not, cannot be thus trifling in character. It must have been one of grave moment; not a slight Variation, but a jump. The successive development of new races — itself, as we have seen, an extremely slow process—must have been continued through numerous steps before the divergence resulting from it could have been serious enough to enable one of the divergent stocks to overcome and exterminate the other. Numerous Species of the same genus now coexist, often within the bounds of a not very extended territory, without any one of them showing any tendency to supplant or exterminate another. Thus, South Africa is the country *par excellence* of the antelope; about fifty species of this animal have been found there, many of them very abundant, notwithstanding the numerous *Carnivora* that prey upon them, and yet none of them showing any tendency to die out before civilized man came thither and brought gunpowder along with him.

Natural Selection can operate only upon races previously brought into being by other causes. In itself, it is powerless either to create or exterminate. In the Development Theory, its only function is, when the number of different Species is so far multiplied that they crowd upon each other, and the extinction of one or more becomes inevitable (if we can conceive of such a case), then to make the *selection*, or to determine which shall be the survivors and which the victims. As individuals of the same Species, the same Variety, and even of the same flock, certainly differ much from each other in strength, swiftness, courage, powers of endurance, and other qualities, Natural Selection has an undoubted part to play, when the struggle comes for such a flock, in determining which of its members shall succumb. But that it ever plays a corresponding part in the grand contest of Species imagined

by Mr. Darwin, is a supposition resting upon no evidence whatever, but only upon the faint presumption afforded by the fact,
that certain Species at widely separated times have become extinct, through what causes we know not; and therefore, for
all that we know to the contrary, Natural Selection may have
had something to do with their disappearance. This is to found
a theory, not upon knowledge, but upon ignorance. If such
reasoning be legitimate, we are entitled to affirm that the moon
is inhabited by men "whose heads do grow beneath their
shoulders." It may be so, for all we know to the contrary.

This review of the state of the evidence upon each of Mr.
Darwin's five points is enough to show that the testimony fails
entirely just where it is most wanted. Facts and arguments are
accumulated where they are of little or no avail, because the
conclusions to which they tend, when properly limited and
qualified, are admitted and familiar principles in science. But
the theory of the Origin of Species by *Cumulative Variation*,
which is all that is peculiar to this form of the transmutation
hypothesis, rests upon no evidence whatever, and has a great
balance of probabilities against it. Individual Variation, the
Struggle for Life, and Natural Selection, each within clearly
defined limits, are acknowledged facts, which still leave the
main question in the philosophy of creation precisely where it
was before; and even the doctrine of Inherited Variation re-
lates only to the *origin* of Varieties, which is a distinct question, and one of subordinate importance and interest, except
to naturalists. Mr. Darwin has invented a new scheme of cosmogony, and finds that, like other cosmogonies, it is a blank
hypothesis, not susceptible either of proof or disproof, and
needing an eternity for its development. There is nothing new
in such a speculation of what is possible in an infinite lapse of
years. This latest form of the speculation has no advantage
over the one first propounded some three thousand years ago;
— that a chaos of atoms, moving about fortuitously in infinite
space, may have happened, in an eternity, to settle into the
present kosmos; for the chance of order and fitness is at least

one out of an infinite number of chances of disorder and confusion; and in an infinite series of years, this solitary chance must sooner or later be realized. . . .

* * *

Every such speculation must be rejected, because it is self-contradictory. It professes to develop a Theory of Creation, — to explain the beginning of things; and in order to do so, it is obliged to assume that the present or ordinary succession of phenomena, the common sequence of causes and effects which we every day witness, has continued from eternity; — that is, that there never was any Creation, and that the universe never began to be. It professes to untie the knot, and ends by denying that there is any knot to untie. Mr. Darwin is too imaginative a thinker to be a safe guide in natural science; he has unconsciously left the proper ground of physics and inductive science, and busied himself with questions of cosmogony and metaphysics.

CHAPTER 4 The Neo-Lamarckian
Transformation

Although evolution may be said to have swept the field of all significant opposition in America by the 1870's, it was at best a hollow victory for the Darwinians. For when Americans accepted evolution, it was not the Darwinian theory of natural selection to which they gave their allegiance, but to a school of thought known as Neo-Lamarckian, or often simply "The American School of Evolution." This school of thought, to which every important American evolutionist before the mid-1890's belonged, assigned a relatively unimportant role to a struggle for existence and, instead, emphasized the direct action of the environment, the inheritance of acquired characteristics, the inherited effect of use and disuse of organs, and the purposeful adaptations of organisms in explaining evolutionary divergence. An article by Joel A. Allen (1838–1921), former student of Agassiz and the curator of birds in the Harvard Museum of Comparative Zoology, summarizes some of the evidence called upon by proponents of the theory.

In part, the American belief in acquired characteristics can be explained as a result of the American specialization in paleontology, and of the certainty of American paleontologists that the fossil layers which they were uncovering provided undeniable evidence that modifications were acquired and handed down to future generations. In the second article

Edward Drinker Cope (1840–1897), a distinguished American paleontologist and one of the founders of the "American School," explains his comprehensive theory of evolution, including his belief in the importance of mental factors. The paleontological evidence in the early years did seem strong, but it was probably not simply a matter of the evidence that persuaded American evolutionists. Since Neo-Lamarckians attributed evolution to an unexplained "vital force" inherent in the organism, rather than to a random process, and since they believed that it followed fixed paths, it was much easier to argue that evolution was theistically directed on their principles than on those of Darwin. In a number of other articles, Cope himself attempted a "reconciliation" of his science with religion.

Blind, non-purposive natural selection also seemed to rule out the "progress" to which Americans were committed with an intensity which has only been shared by one other society on earth. The other society is, of course, Soviet Russia, and it is probably significant that until the late 1940's, orthodox evolutionary theory in Russia was also Neo-Lamarckian.

The importance placed upon the environment by Neo-Lamarckians with the manipulative possibilities that this suggested, was quite in keeping with traditional American social attitudes. American social thought has historically been strongly environmental, imbued with the faith, handed down from the Enlightenment, that there are no bad people — only bad circumstances. In order to improve humanity, one has only to improve its conditions of life. As the selection from Joseph LeConte illustrates, there were cogent nonscientific reasons why it was important to believe that improvements of this generation would be passed down to the next. The material reprinted here was added to the second edition of LeConte's book (1891), written after his school of evolutionary thought had come under attack, and after most of its scientific basis had been destroyed. The fact that a distinguished scientist would add such an argument as a kind of last-ditch stand strongly indicates the socially conditioned nature of much scientific thought.

In America the school began to crumble in the 1890's, as the theoretical supports began to be taken from it by continuing research, mostly in Europe. While it flourished, however, it made evolution palatable to large numbers of people who would never have accepted it otherwise. It thus served an important function in the history of American science — as well as in American social history.

JOEL A. ALLEN
The Influence of Physical Conditions in the Genesis of Species, *The Radical Review*, 1, 1877–1878, pp. 108–137

Among biologists who accept the modern theory of evotion as the only reasonable hypothesis available for the explanation of the diversity of structure among organized beings, there is a wide difference of opinion as to what are the leading causes of differentiation. The doctrine of natural selection, or the survival of the fittest, has recently been brought prominently forward as the key to this complex problem, and is upheld by a large class of enthusiastic adherents, who accept it as the full solution of the whole question. By others the conditions of environment are believed to be far more influential in effecting a certain class of modification, at least, than the necessarily precarious influence of natural selection, which must take its origin in isolated instances of variation in favorable directions, and depend for its continuance upon these fortuitous advantages being inherited by the descendants of the favored individuals in which they originate. The modifying influence of conditions resulting from geographic or climatic causes, was long since noticed, and for nearly a century has been considered by many writers as explanatory of much of the diversity existing not only in the human race, but among animals. It has, however, remained,

until recently, vaguely grounded, being based more in conjecture than on observed facts. . . . In the work of registering
these instructive data, it has fallen to Americans to take a
leading part; large credit in the matter being due not only to
the activity of our professional biologists, but to the liberality
of the general Government in attaching competent natural-
history observers and collectors to the accumulation of an
amount of material far exceeding that elsewhere accessible to
single investigators; . . . Upon [the American data] have been
based hypotheses that go far toward explaining many of the
phenomena of intergradation and differentiation observed
among existing animals. . . . These results, it is claimed, show
that other influences than natural selection operate powerfully
in the differentiation of specific forms, and that geographical
causes share more largely in the work than naturalists have
heretofore been prepared to admit, — at least to consider as
proven. . . .

*   *   *

The local races of any given region, as compared collec-
tively with those of contiguous regions, and the manner of
their mutual intergradation, point plainly to some general or
widely acting cause of differentiation. This is indicated by the
constancy of the results, so many species, belonging to numerous and widely distinct groups, being similarly affected.
Will the fortuitous, spontaneous results of natural selection
yield a satisfactory explanation of these phenomena, or must
we seek some more uniform and definitely acting cause? To
briefly summarize the results above detailed, we have a somewhat uniform increase of size in some given direction affecting
many species simultaneously and similarly over the same areas.
We have a frequent enlargement of peripheral parts, affecting
not a few but many species, and all in a similar manner, though
in varying degrees. We have a very general increase in the
depth or intensity of colors southward, a general loss of color

in approaching the central, arid portions of the continent, and again an excessive increment of color under still different climatic conditions and over a different area. We find the increase of size among the individuals of any given species to be quite uniformly in the direction of the center of distribution of the group to which the species belongs, this being especially well-marked in mammals. We find the increase in the size of peripheral parts, — as the external ear and the length of the pelage in mammals, and the size of the bill and length of the tail in birds, — to be in the direction of the regions where these parts meet respectively their greatest development, — the increase in color (especially among birds) toward the region where are developed the richest and most lustrous tints, the loss of color in the direction of the region where the greatest general pallor prevails. We find again that the enlargement of peripheral parts correlates with an increase of atmospheric humidity and temperature, and consequently with the protective influences of luxuriant arboreal vegetation and clouds; and, conversely, the loss of color accompanying excessive aridity, a scanty vegetation, and an almost cloudless sky, — the conditions, in short, of all others the most powerfully effective in the blanching of color; and again the sombre, dusky tints of the north-west coast accompanying the most favorable for the protection or preservation of color. Are these merely accidental coincidences, or are they the evident results of cause and effect? Because the white winter livery of some of the northern species is more protective against cold than darker tints would be, or aids in concealing them in some cases (as in the hares and ptarmigans) from their enemies, or in other cases (as in the ermines and the Arctic fox) tends to aid them in stealing unperceived upon their prey, are they to be regarded as unquestionably the beneficial results of the working of natural selection? Because the dull gray tints of species inhabiting the semi-desert regions of the interior harmonize well with the general gray aspect of their surroundings, is this concordance the result again of the operation of the law of natural selection, the less favorably colored having been weeded out in the struggle for existence? Are the heavy, dull colors of the humid region of the north-west the result, again, of the necessary influence of natural selection in perpetuating only the individuals whose colors best accord with their sombre conditions of environment? Has the same action brought about the bright, rich coloration of birds, insects, and other animals under the warm humid conditions of the hotter parts of the earth, preserving the ratio of brilliancy of coloration with that of the conditions that everywhere most favor such differentiation? Finally, is the exact correlation of the changes in coloration with the gradual change of climatic conditions in passing from one geographical region to another the result in like manner of the long-continued weeding out of the less-favored? Or are these modifications severally due to the *direct* action of the conditions of environment? . . .

*   *   *

[Even assuming, according to the theory of natural selection, that favorable variations do appear] there are many adverse circumstances with which the favored forms have in the outset to contend, and to which, in the majority of instances, they must succumb. These are, first, the minuteness of the first favorable divergence, the isolation of the individuals in which it appears, and consequently the impossibility of such individuals pairing with others similarly favored, and the consequent tendency of the offspring to possess the favorable characters in a less rather than in a greater degree than the parent, and to be absorbed into the original stock.* Secondly, in case the incipient advantages are perpetuated, as it is necessary to suppose, the new offshoot must originate from a single

---

* Allen is referring to the phenomenon of "swamping." As noted in an earlier context, this was not shown to be impossible before the rediscovery of Mendelian genetics.

point, and spread thence gradually to contiguous regions as its representatives slowly multiply. . . .

* * *

The direct influence of climatic or geographical conditions upon animals is, in the main, ignored by the leading exponents of the doctrine of natural selection. . . .

There is, however, a vast amount of unquestionable proof of the direct and constant action of climate and other conditions of life upon animals, and that such geographical variations as the thicker and softer fur of mammals inhabiting cold regions, smaller size and brighter colors at the southward, etc., etc., do not require the action of natural selection, in its strict and proper sense, for their explanation. It is well known, for instance, that a flock of fine-wooled sheep, when taken to a hot climate, rapidly acquire a coarser and coarser fleece, till, in a few generations, it nearly loses its character of proper wool, and becomes simply hair; that the change affects simultaneously the whole flock, and is not brought about by one or two individuals acquiring a coarser fleece and through their descendants modifying the character of the herd. . . .

* * *

While so much is claimed by the writer as due to the direct action of climatic causes, it is admitted also that habits and food, and other conditions of life than those resulting from climate, have a marked effect in determining modifications of form and color among animals. A scarcity of a favorite kind of food will undoubtedly force species to subsist upon the next best that offers, which may be so different as to modify certain characters and fit the species to live upon the less desired food. A change of food may lead to modification of dentition, the muscles of mastication, and the organs of digestion, and, correlatively, of other organs or parts of the body; the modification, however, arising simultaneously among all the descendants of the individuals thus driven to a change of

diet, instead of appearing first in a single individual and becoming perpetuated in its descendants alone. Entomologists
have found that, among insects of the same species, the forced
or voluntary use of different food-plants gives rise to modifications of color and structure, and hence results in what have
been termed phytophagic varieties or sub-species, and that
man can also effect such changes at will by simply changing
the food of the species. Again, the geological character of a
country is well known to have a marked effect upon the size
and color of animals inhabiting it, as is strikingly illustrated
among molluscous animals, whose abundance, and even presence, is largely dependent upon the constituents of the soil.
Over regions of the United States, for example, where the
underlying rock is non-calcareous, the species are both few
in number and sparsely represented, while in other regions,
where limestone abounds, but which are in other respects
essentially the same, the species are far more numerous and far
more abundantly represented. . . .

*   *   *

Use and disuse of organs, through changes of habit resulting
from changed conditions of environment, must result in some
modification of the organ involved. As an example may doubt-
less be cited the passerine birds of some of the smaller, re-
motely-situated islands, as the Guadeloupe and Galapagos
groups, where recent investigations have shown that most of
the species differ similarly in several features from their nearest
allies of the mainland, and of which they are unquestionably
insular forms. These differences consist in the greater size of
the bill, shorter wings, longer tails, and darker colors. The
sedentary life necessitated by the confined habitats of species
thus situated would naturally act more or less strongly on the
organs of flight, and a reduction in the size of the wing would
follow; — not necessarily through the round-about process of
natural selection, through the modification originally of a

single individual, but by the direct action on all the individuals alike of the changed conditions of life. . . .

*   *   *

Much has been written respecting the influence of climate on man, and many speculations have been indulged in in relation to the part the conditions of life have taken in bringing about the diversity at present existing among the different races. A striking parallelism is often observable between the leading features of geographical variation among animals and the physical differences that obtain among nations or races of men inhabiting the same areas and subjected to the same influences. While civilized man is, in a measure, less the subject of such influences than the lower animals, he is not wholly above them. Certain regions more favor both physical and intellectual development than others; and these prove to be, as would be expected, the milder temperate portions of the globe, where the struggle for a mere vegetative existence is reduced to a minimum.

The influence of different climatic conditions upon members of the same nationality find exemplification in different parts of our own country, and are so obvious as to be the subject of frequent observation and comment. The same original stock is found to gradually develop certain peculiar physical and mental characteristics when placed under diverse conditions of climate, certain localities more favoring intellectual growth and activity than others; just as certain regions are characterized by the frequent occurrence of particular diseases, which in other regions are exceptional. While humidity and a high temperature when combined, are found to be enervating and deteriorating, a clear dry atmosphere favors vigor of both mind and body. But the subject of the influence of climatic conditions upon man is too vast to be entered upon in detail in the present connection. The study of man from a geographical standpoint, or with special reference to conditions of environment, offers a most important and fruitful field of research, which, it is to be hoped, will soon receive a more careful attention than has as yet been given it. . . .

EDWARD DRINKER COPE
Evolution and Its Consequences, *Penn Monthly Magazine*, *May*, *July, August 1872, as reprinted in Cope,* Origin of the Fittest: Essays on Evolution, *New York, D. Appleton & Co., 1887, pp. 1–40*

. . . It is plain that the useful additions which have constituted certain genera, families, orders, etc., . . . must have been produced as a consequence of the existence of a need for them; or, on the other hand, being created first, they must have sought for use, and found it. But what are the relative chances of truth for these two propositions? In the second case, admitting evolution as proved, we perceive that an almost infinite chance exists against any usual amount of variation, as observed, producing a structure which shall be fit to survive in consequence of its superior adaptation to external circumstances. It would be incredible that a blind or undirected variation should not fail in a vast majority of instances to produce a single case of the beautiful adaptation to means and ends which we see so abundantly around us. The amount of attempt, failure, and consequent destruction, would be preposterously large, and in no wise consistent with the facts of teleology as we behold them.

What of the opposite view? . . . Who has not remarked the large size of the hands of the laborer, and of the nails of the working-woman? Who can not remember some of the countless examples of certain modifications of form being associated with special excellence of use of the parts in different races of the same species of individuals of common parentage, showing that they must have grown with the history of those races? Who does not know the short, wide jaws of the bull-dog, with their oblique teeth, produced by the expansion of the zygomata to accommodate the huge temporal muscles so necessary for maintaining a firm hold of its enemy. Then the long and full nose of the hound, and its more extended turbinate bones — how closely is this connected with its developed scent; while the light muscular forms of the greyhound are undoubtedly necessary to its well-known speed. . . .

*   *   *

Another reason for believing in use as a cause of structural change is the manner in which the same useful structures have evidently appeared on totally distinct systems, as an evident adaptation to the same circumstances in which the different types have been equally placed. Thus the birds of prey possess the hooked, often toothed, beak, appropriate for tearing and destroying animals. Their stock is the same as that of the cuckoos and parrots, and even of the pigeons. The butcher-birds are of the division of songsters, not widely removed from the thrushes, and far enough from the raptores, yet the same hook and dentate bill reappears in them, as adapted to flesh-eating habits. . . .

*   *   *

For these and other reasons it is concluded that the useful characters, defining natural divisions of animals, have been produced by the special "location of growth-force" by use. Useless ones have been produced by location of growth-force without the influence of use, or by its subtraction, due to a disturbance of equilibrium, consequent on the special location elsewhere. . . .

*   *   *

There is, however, another element which in animals disturbs the symmetrical direction of growth-force besides use, and which precedes use, i.e., effort. Use presupposes a part to use, and a simple part is sufficient for its influence, so that it be *usable;* but the first beginnings of few structures are usable.

. . . it might be urged against the theory of use that rudiments are generally *useless*, and could not have been originated by use.

The effect of use is, however, twofold. The contact with objects used has some effect in stimulating nutrition, as well as the exertion of the muscles necessary to use. But determination of nutritive fluid is well known to be under the influence of nerve-force. How imagination stimulates secretion is seen in the familiar example of the flow of saliva in anticipation of food; a very different example is the phenomenon of blushing under emotional stimulus. Nevertheless, it is not evident that growth can result with any such facility in a fully grown animal. It is thought that the effort becomes incorporated into the metaphysical acquisitions of the parent, and is inherited with other metaphysical qualities by the young, which during the period of growth is much more susceptible to modifying influences and is likely to exhibit structural change in consequence. Certain it is that acceleration ceases with growth, and, as the young of animals are not in complete relation with the surrounding world, the influences controlling it must be inherited. This consideration renders it doubly probable that the results of effort on the part of the parent appear in change of structure in the offspring. . . .

*   *   *

[*Cope then argues that mental characteristics are heritable in the same manner as physical, and passes on to a consideration of the role of mind in directing evolution.*]

Leaving this part of the subject, we approach one of higher interest, viz., the effects of the metaphysical or mental acquirements of animals on their exertions in effort and use. The growth of the mind in animals has, no doubt, followed the same laws obeyed by that of man; the difference being that the lower forms have remained permanently fixed in stages early passed by the lord of living beings. The foundation qualities from which all the phenomena of intellect may be derived are, the powers of retentiveness (memory) and of perceptions of resemblance and difference. These traits are well known to be possessed by many animals, and perhaps in some degree by all. Their possession will be modified by the power of exercising *attention*, which, in turn, will depend on the sensitiveness of the animal to impressions — in other words, the ease with which the consciousness may be aroused.

The origin of the disposition to take food will be the rudiment of all that appears as *will* in higher animals, and which, though supposed to guide, is the creature of so many *stimuli*. This origin is supposed by metaphysicians to be the result of education of the "spontaneous activity" of animals by their pleasures and pains.

The brain of man and of other animals is an organ which receives and retains pictures and impressions, both painful and pleasurable. The retention of these pictures is not a state of consciousness, but they may be brought into the consciousness according to the law of "contiguity," or association. That is, that the recurrence in the actual of some object or event, which was perceived on a former occasion, at or near the same time as another object or event not again repeated in the actual, will bring the latter before the consciousness. So, also, the revival of one such picture will bring within the mental vision others impressed on the mind at or near the same time as the first. These events may have been in the reality either painful or pleasurable. On the recurrence of circumstances which on a former occasion resulted in pain, the resuscitation of the mental picture, then impressed on the memory, produces an anticipation of the pain, and the animal at once flies from the source of danger. So, also, with pleasurable objects, the resultant action being the reverse, or an attraction to the object. In both cases a previous experience of the relation between the object and the sensation of pleasure or pain must have been had. . . .

* * *

All intellectual functions are produced by education, and education involves consciousness at every step. Other habitual and automatic acts were originated consciously, but the contiguity of parts of the act becoming impressed on the brain, future repetitions of it are reflex or unconscious. We have seen that the development of the habits of animals is in strict obedience to the preference for pleasure and avoidance of pain. Pleasures and pains of course express sensations which involve consciousness. It then appears to me that, in the lowest animal, consciousness must be present at the time of origin of every habit, but that it may have been soon lost in each case, and the habit become automatic.

If this position be true, every subsequent addition to or change of habits must have been accompanied by a resuscitation of consciousness. . . .

*   *   *

In the history of the material environment, various changes of condition succeeded each other. Changes of level took place; waters were purified by precipitation of chemical compounds; fresh·waters were established; the atmosphere deprived of various gases; new mineral, and especially vegetable, products took their appropriate places. All these offer a vast variety of food-supply and opportunity for the pleasurable discharge of motive-force, and, under the laws pointed out, efforts of animals were directed in various lines, as the conditions presented themselves. Thus executive organs were produced of various character. Some acquired limbs and others wings for transportation from place to place. What a vast addition to their impressions must have been acquired by the first animals which could thus leave the place of their birth! How many new "contiguities" were established, and how many new habits originated! Look again at the acquisition of teeth. From a soft uniform diet the animal no doubt gradually learned to appropriate hard substances, and what a world of experience and consequent habit must have been at once placed in its way!

These acquisitions are of course mental, and include both kinds of contiguity, viz., that of succession in time, and that of association through resemblance. Animals choose between objects chiefly in accordance with the first mode, but are not lacking in the second quality. As an example of the latter, classification according to color is exhibited by some birds, which choose brightly colored objects and reject dull ones — the Australian bower-bird for instance.

As is well known to metaphysicians, these acquisitions lead to "predication" and "forethought." Thus a hound becomes acquainted with the habit of a buck or rabbit in doubling, or in following a given circuit. The recurrence of the chase recalls the habit in consequence of contiguity of the impression of the former pursuit of the animal and the course it took. The hound then supposes or "predicates" that the deer will repeat the course. We know that some do so from the fact that they have been observed to cut off the curves in the animal's track, or to station themselves at the point where the deer, for instance, will pass. In the second act forethought is also involved. The hound sacrifices the lesser pleasure of the chase for the greater one of securing the prey. In forethought, experience having taught which circumstance results in greater and which in less pleasure, action is restrained in the presence of the second for the sake of procuring the first. Thus in ants, immediate pleasure suggests a life of labor enough for present wants, and ease for the remaining time; but the greater pleasure of existence during some time of scarcity has induced some of them to lay up a store, which has developed into the complete protection against winter they display in cold climates.

In the cases cited it is perfectly evident that the hound would never have learned to predicate had he not had limbs to bring him in contact (by pursuit) with the habits of the

buck. Nor would the ant have learned to provide if it had not
been furnished with the jaws necessary to the excavation of
chambers and the carrying of food. And neither would have
performed these mental acts had they not possessed nervous
centers capable of sensation, retention, and classification. But
the development of these qualities depended on the possession
of the executive organs.

Thus intelligence of various degrees has resulted — first,
from possession of executive organs; secondly, establishment
of contiguities by their use; thirdly, from classifications based
on contiguities. . . .

*   *   *

To return to the material aspect of the case. The discrimi-
nation between pleasure and pain locates motive-force, which
is derived from without. Motion or use locates growth-force,
also derived from without, and thus produces organs out of
material derived from without. These organs diversify the
directions of motion. From new movements arise new pleasures and pains, and motion is again "located" in its exhibitions
in some particular directions, and restrained in others. These
directions depend on external circumstances at the first. The
determination of motion to certain lines locates growth-force
in those lines, and new parts are produced, which are further
executive organs and types of structure. We now repeat the
circuit. New executive organs introduce new contiguities, the
number depending on the general complication of the animal
in connection with that of the organ, and new pleasures and
pains result. The pleasures again determine activity, and, under the circumstances already mentioned, growth-force is
again located. . . .

*   *   *

These conjunctions of growth with executive capacity, constitute a class of "expression points"; points attained without

leaps, and abandoned without abruptness, but constituting great steps of progress, pregnant with future results.

The part played by "intelligent selection" remains to be considered. . . .

*   *   *

Intelligence is a conservative principle, and always will direct effort and use into lines which will be beneficial to its possessor. Here we have the source of the fittest — i.e., addition of parts by increase and location of growth-force, directed by the influence of various kinds of compulsion in the lower, and intelligent option among higher animals.

Thus, intelligent choice, taking advantage of the successive evolution of physical conditions, may be regarded as the *originator of the fittest*, while natural selection is the tribunal to which all the results of accelerated growth are submitted. This preserves or destroys them, and determines the new points of departure on which accelerated growth shall build.

If the above positions be true, we have here also the theory of the development of intelligence and of other metaphysical traits. In accordance with it, each trait appropriates from the material world the means of perpetuating its exhibitions by constructing its instruments. These react by furnishing increased means of exercise of these qualities, which have thus grown to their full expression in man.

JOSEPH LECONTE
The Grades of the Factors of Evolution and the Order of Their Appearance, *Evolution: Its Nature, Its Evidences, and Its Relation to Religious Thought, 2nd ed., New York, D. Appleton & Co., 1891*

I. Evolution, as a law of derivation of organic forms from previous forms by descent with modifications, as already shown, is as certain as the law of gravitation. This question has passed beyond the realm of doubtful discussion; but the causes, the factors, the details of the process of evolution are still under discussion. Both Darwin and Spencer, the two great founders of the theory of evolution in its modern form, acknowledge and insist on at least four factors, viz., the two Lamarckian and the two distinctively Darwinian. The only difference between them is in the relative importance of the two sets: Spencer regarding the former and Darwin the latter as the more potent. But in these latest times there has arisen a class of biologists, including some of highest rank, such as Wallace, Weismann, and Lankester,* who out-Darwin Darwin himself in their exaltation of the most distinctive factor, viz., natural selection. They try to show that natural selection is the sole and sufficient cause of evolution; that changes in the individual, whether as the effect of the environment or by use and disuse of organs, are not inherited at all; that Lamarck was wholly wrong; that Darwin (in connection with Wallace) was the sole founder of the true theory of evolution; and, finally, that Darwin himself was wrong only in making any terms whatever with Lamarck. This view has been called *Neo-Darwinism.* . . .

*   *   *

We have already given the views of Weismann and Wallace, and some reasons for not accepting them; but there is one important aspect not yet touched. There are some logical consequences of these views when applied to human evolution which seem to us nothing less than a *reductio ad absurdum.*

---

* August Weismann (1834–1914), a German biologist best known as the originator of the germ-plasm theory of heredity, the concept that germ-plasm constitutes the only organic connection between one generation and the next, and that the hereditary substance of the germ cells is completely independent of changes in the external environment.

Edwin Ray Lankester (1847–1927), a British comparative anatomist and evolutionist, was at one time the director of the Natural History Museum, London.

This brings into view still another contrast between organic evolution and human progress.

In organic evolution, when the struggle for life is fierce and pitiless as it is now among the higher animals, natural selection is undoubtedly by far the most potent factor. It is at least conceivable (though not probable) that at the present time organic evolution might be carried on mainly or even wholly by this factor alone; but in human evolution, especially in civilized communities, this is impossible. If Weismann and Wallace be right, then alas for all our hopes of race improvement — physical, mental, and moral! — for natural selection will never be applied by man to himself as it is by Nature to organisms. His spiritual nature forbids. Reason may freely use the Lamarckian factors of environment and of use and disuse, but is debarred the unscrupulous use of natural selection *as its only method*. As this is an important point, we must explain.

All enlightened schemes of physical culture and hygiene, although directed primarily to secure the strength, the health, and the happiness of the *present generation*, yet are sustained and ennobled by the conviction that the improvement of the individuals of each generation enters by inheritance into the gradual physical improvement of the race. All our schemes of education, intellectual and moral, though certainly intended mainly for the improvement of the individual, are glorified by the hope that the race also is thereby gradually elevated. It is true that these hopes are usually extravagant; it is true that the *whole* improvement of one generation is not carried over by inheritance into the next; it is true, therefore, that we can not by education raise a lower race up to the plane of a higher in a few generations or even in a few centuries: but there must be at least a small residuum, be it ever so small, carried forward from each generation to the next, which, accumulating from age to age, determines the slow evolution of the race. Such are the hopes on which all noble efforts for race-improvement are founded. Are all these hopes baseless? They are so if Weismann and Wallace are right. If it be true that reason must direct the course of human progress, and if it be true also that selection of the fittest in the organic sense is the only method which can be used by reason, then the dreadful law of pitiless destruction of the weak, the helpless, the sick, the old, must with Spartan firmness be voluntarily and deliberately carried out. Against such a course we instinctively revolt with horror, because [it is] contrary to the law of our spiritual nature.

But the use by reason of the Lamarckian factors is not attended with any such revolting consequences. All our hopes of race-improvement, therefore, are strictly conditioned on the efficacy of these factors — i.e., on the fact that useful changes, determined by education in each generation, are to some extent inherited and accumulated in the race.

The Religious
CHAPTER 5 Accommodation to
Darwinism

Once a modified Darwinism became orthodox among American scientists, most religious thinkers quickly accommodated themselves to the theory. Of course, there did remain some, such as Charles Hodge, who continued to proclaim to the end of his days that Darwinism was atheism. And there remained also a residue of fundamentalist thought which reemerged in the 1920's. But by far the majority of leading religious thinkers worked out an early accommodation with Darwinism in some fashion. Probably the healthiest reaction was that represented by James McCosh (1811–1894), a world famous philosopher who came from Scotland to accept the presidency of Princeton in 1868. McCosh, in accepting the theory of evolution, modified by the "softer" elements introduced by the Neo-Lamarckians, insisted that his theology was not fundamentally affected. For him, the program of evolution simply magnified the wonder and the mystery of the process of Creation. God was just as real as He had been before Darwin, and Christianity was little affected.

McCosh and others like him, however, had long since moved beyond a need for any Biblical literalism. For those who had not, the accommodation was often grotesque, resulting in a strained "reconciliation" of Biblical passages to make the facts of evolution fit them. The brief extract from an anonymous author simply states the program of the literalists. The Bible, being inspired, had given an absolutely true "outline" of the scientific facts; science could only fill in the details which God had not deigned to reveal to the benighted Hebrews. The two articles by C. B. Warring illustrate how much it was possible to do with this license. Most modern readers will be inclined to think that if the Bible is as wondrously plastic as Warring interprets it, there is little meaning in the claim that it is "inspired truth."

A third form of accommodation, and the one that became extremely popular in the last quarter of the nineteenth century, was to elaborate an entirely new — and often bizarre — theology on the basis of what the writer thought to be the "permanent" core of Christianity. God was often seen as simply another name for the evolutionary process itself, or perhaps the "unknowable" cosmic force standing behind the evolutionary process. The essential point in these interpretations is that either the universe itself or some scientific process was taken for both the Deity and the source of morality. This reaction is best illustrated by John Fiske, popular lecturer, historian and cosmic philosopher. His personal version of an ultimate reconciliation between science and religion appeared in his two volume *Outlines of Cosmic Philosophy* (1874). The present selection is from an after dinner speech delivered at a banquet for the English philosopher Herbert Spencer in 1882. Note that this speech also contains Fiske's characteristic confusion between "evolution" and "progress."

JAMES MCCOSH

Religious Aspects of the Doctrine of Development, *P. Schaff and S. Prime (eds.), History, Essays, Orations, and Other Documents of the Sixth General Conference of the Evangelical Alliance, Held in New York, October 2–12, 1873, New York, 1874, pp. 269–271*

All that science has demonstrated, all that theism has argued, of the order, of the final cause and benevolent purpose in the world is true, and can not be set aside. Every natural law —

mechanical, chemical, and vital — is good. Every organ of the
body, when free from disease, is good. There is certainly the
most exquisite adaptation in the eye, however we may account
for its formation, and for the numerous diseases which seize
upon it. Agassiz has shown, by an induction of facts reaching
over the whole history of the animal kingdom, that there is
plan in the succession of organic life. "It has the correspondence of connected plan. It is just that kind of resemblance in
the parts — so much and no more — as always characterizes
intellectual work proceeding from the same source. It has that
freedom of manifestation, that independence, which characterizes the work of mind, as compared with the work of law.
Sometimes in looking at the epos of organic life in its totality,
carried on with such care and variety, and even playfulness of
expression, one is reminded of the great conception of the poet
or musician, where the undertone of the fundamental harmony
is heard beneath all the diversity of rhythm or song." All this
is true, but all this is not all the truth. What the older scientific men did not see — what Newton did not see, as he looked
to the perfect order of the heavens — what Cuvier did not see,
when he dwelt so fondly on the teleology seen in every part of
the animal structure — what Paley did not see, when he
pointed out the design in every bone, in every joint and muscle
— what Chalmers did not see, when in his astronomical dis-
courses he sought to reconcile the perfection of the heavens
with the need of God's providing a Saviour for men — has
been forced on our notice, as naturalists have been searching
into animal life, with its struggles and its sufferings. There *is*
order in our world, but it is order subordinating conflicting
powers. There is goodness — but goodness overcoming evil.
There is progression — but progression like that of the ship on
the ocean, amid winds and waves. There is the certainty of
peace — but after a battle and a victory. There may be seen
everywhere an overruling power in bringing good out of evil;
so that Schopenhauer, in noticing the evil, has noticed only a
part, and this only a subordinate part of the whole — and this
to be ultimately swallowed up.

While they have seen the phenomenon, these men have not known what to make of it. It is useless to tell the younger naturalists that there is no truth in the doctrine of development, for they know that there is truth, which is not to be set aside by denunciation. Religious philosophers might be more profitably employed in showing them the religious aspects of the doctrine of development; and some would be grateful to any who would help them to keep their old faith in God and the Bible with their new faith in science. But we must at the same time point out the necessary limits of the doctrine, and rebuke those unwise because conceited men who, when they have made a few observations in one department of physical nature, being commonly profoundly ignorant of every other — particularly of mental and moral science — imagine that they can explain everything by the one law of evolution. But there is a large and important body of facts which these hypotheses can not cover. Development implies an original matter with high endowments. Whence the original matter? It is acknowledged, by its most eminent expounder, that evolution can not account for the first appearance of life. Greatly to the disappointment of some of his followers, Darwin is obliged to postulate three or four germs of life created by God. To explain the continuance of life, he is obliged to call in a pangenesis, or universal life, which is just a vague phrase for that inexplicable thing life, and life is just a mode of God's action. Plants, the first life that appeared, have no sensation. How did sensation come in? Whence animal instinct? Whence affection — the affection of a mother for her offspring, of a patriot for his country, of a Christian for his Saviour? Whence intelligence? Whence discernment of duty as imperative? It is felt by all students of mental science that Darwin is weak when he seeks to account for these high ideas and sentiments. Careful, as being so trained, in noticing the minutest peculiarities of plants and animals, and acquainted as he has made himself with the appetites and habits of animals, he seems utterly incapable of understanding man's higher capacities and noble aspirations — of seeing how much is involved in consciousness, in personal identity, in necessary truth, in unbending rectitude; he explains them only by overlooking their essential peculiarities. It is allowed that geology does not show an unbroken descent of the lower animals from the higher; on the contrary, it is ever coming to breaks, and, in the case of a number of tribes of the lower animals, the more highly organized forms appear first, and are followed by a degeneracy. It is acknowledged that in the historical ages we do not see such new endowments coming in by natural law — the plant becoming animal, or the monkey becoming man. That matter should of itself develop into thought is a position which neither observation nor reason sanctions. Science gives no countenance to it. Common-sense turns away from it. Philosophy declares that this would be an effect without a cause adequate to produce it.

But these inquiries have brought us face to face with a remarkable body of facts. The known effects in the world — the order, beauty, and beneficence — point to the nature and character of their cause; and this not an unknown God, as Herbert Spencer maintains, but a known God. "The invisible things of God from the creation of the world are clearly seen, being understood from the things that are made, even his eternal power and Godhead." But in the very midst of the good there is evil: the good is shown in removing the evil, in relieving suffering, in solacing sorrow, and conquering sin. Evil, properly speaking, can not appear till there are animated beings, and as soon as sentient life appears there is pain, which is an evil. It does look as if in the midst of arrangements contrived with infinite skill there is some derangement. It may turn out that the Bible doctrine, so much ridiculed in the present day, of there being a Satan, an adversary, opposed to God and good, has a deep foundation in the nature of things, even as it has confirmation in our experience without and within us, where we find that when we would do good, evil is present with us. . . . How curious, should it turn out that these scientific inquirers, so laboriously digging in the earth, have, all unknown to themselves, come upon the missing link which is partially to reconcile natural and revealed religion. Our English Titan is right when he says that at the basis of all phenomena we come to something unknown and unknowable. He would erect an altar to the unknown God, and Professor Huxley would have the worship paid there to be chiefly of the silent sort. But a Jew, born at Tarsus, no mean city in Greek philosophy, and brought up at the feet of Gamaliel — but subdued, on the road to Damascus, by a greater teacher than any in Greece or Jewry — told the men of Athens, who had erected an altar to the unknown God, "Whom ye ignorantly worship, him I declare unto you." It does look as if later science had come in view of the darkness brooding on the face of the deep without knowing of the wind of the Spirit which is to dispel it, and divide the evil from the good, and issue in a spiritual creation, of which the first or natural creation was by a type.

We do not as yet see all things reconciled between these two sides — the side of Scripture and the side of science. But we see enough to satisfy us that the two correspond. It is the same world, seen under different aspects. We see in both the most skillful arrangement; we are told in both of some derangement. Both reveal a known God; both bring us to an unknown source of evil. But with the sameness there is a difference. The relation is not one of identity, but of correspondence; like that of the earth to the concave sky by which it is canopied; like that of the movement of the dial on earth to that of the sun in heaven. On this side is a wail from the deepest heart of the sufferer; on that side there is consolation from the deepest heart of a comforter. On the one side is a cry like that of the young bird when it feels that it has wandered from its dam; and the other, a call like that of the mother bird, as you may hear her in the evening, to bring her wandering ones under her wings. You may notice on that side a bier, with a corpse laid out upon it of a youth, the only son of his mother, and she a widow; on that other side the same picture, but with one touching the bier, and the dead arises and is in the embraces of his mother. On this side you see a sepulchre, and all men in the end consigned to it, and none coming out of it; on the other side you see the great stone rolled away, and hear a voice, "He is not here; He is risen." The grand reconciliation is effected by that central figure standing in the middle of the ages, by Him who has "made peace through the blood of his cross, by Him to reconcile all things unto Himself, by Him, I say, whether they be things on earth or things in heaven."

ANONYMOUS
The Sixth Day of Creation, *Boston Review*, *III, 1863, pp. 68–69*

As Orthodox reviewers, we cannot admit the claim of some geologists, that the Mosaic account of the creation is to be set aside as inconsistent with some of their alleged facts. We readily admit that, where inspiration has given us a mere outline, geology, or any other human science, may fill up that outline with well-ascertained facts, if it can; and the details thus supplied, though they cannot become articles of religious faith, will have all the certainty that belongs to them in science, and an additional presumption in their favor, in proportion as they naturally and perfectly fit into and fill out the inspired outline. We also concede, that where inspiration uses terms which logicians call general, and which are equally capable of either of several specific meanings, geology may, if it can, show us in which of those specific meanings the general term is to be taken. In all this, there is no inconsistency between the inspired declaration and the geological showing. We will even concede that geology may, without impiety or irreverence, ask us to reconsider an old and generally received interpretation of a passage of Scripture, which it knows not how to reconcile with its apparent discoveries; and that it may be lawful, and even a duty, to comply with the request; and if the old interpretation is found to rest on erroneous or insufficient

grounds, and a new interpretation presents itself, equally justified by the language of Scripture, and in harmony with the
discovery of geology, we may receive it as true. But in such
a case, the new interpretation must be one which we might
receive and defend if geology had been silent. In no case can
geology be allowed to contradict the words of the Sacred
Record rightly interpreted, or to force upon them an unnat-
ural interpretation by its own authority. Wherever there is
an actual contradiction between the facts of geology and the
words of inspiration properly interpreted, geology is wrong,
and needs to reconsider its facts.

C.   B.   W A R R I N G
Genesis and "Science," *The Christian Advocate, New York, March
7, 1878 and March 14, 1878*

There is at the present day a great change in the mode of
the attacks upon the Bible. We hear little more of "historical
blunders," nor does any scholar deem it wise to assert that the
text has been corrupted. Arguments which a few years ago
were urged so confidently are now ignored, and their places
supplied by others based upon the greater physical knowledge
of the present day. By the audacity and persistence of their
attacks, the opponents of revelation have so alarmed some of
the believers in the Bible, that, to escape from the dilemma in
which they imagined themselves placed, they have surrendered
all that claims to be inspired in the Mosaic account of creation,
save some general truths as to God's creatorship. They have
even dared to style it, . . . "poetical, symbolical and unchronological." They thus, it is true, avoid assaults based upon what
they have been told, and too readily have admitted, are con-
tradictions between Genesis and science, but they expose it to
other attacks of a different, but not less dangerous, character.
The question would soon be raised. If such a series of statements as this, made apparently in sober earnest without a
suggestion of metaphor, proves to be merely a moral lesson

teaching through allegory God's creatorship and the observance of the Sabbath, what is there of all that we have been wont to regard as history which may not in like manner fade away into poetry or fable?

For one, I am not going to give up this grand old account until I am compelled to. Reasons that have no connection with astronomy or geology force me to accept the Bible as a revelation from God, and hence, *prima facie*, I accept that first chapter of Genesis even though I may not wholly understand it. I do this every day for hundreds of physical matters which my senses bring to my knowledge. I believe, also, that "science," so far as it is true, is likewise from God, and hence, that when it has advanced far enough, the agreement of the two will become manifest to all. And as all the physical sciences, particularly astronomy and geology, have made wonderful progress during the last half century. I am confident those who have kept abreast of them are in a better position than ever before to discover and demonstrate the absolute agreement of the two records, so far as each goes. To do this it will be necessary to let Moses tell his own story, or, in other words, to drop all expositions which assume to tell us what he *meant* to say — this is a very hard lesson — and to adhere most closely to what he does say — another very hard lesson. I would hold to these two principles with the utmost rigidness, for Moses has too long been condemned for what he never wrote. Nor would I vary from the rule so far as to hold him responsible for what good men have honestly thought was implied in what he has said. These are common rules in every court of justice. Hence, before attempting to answer an objector who should claim that Moses errs in any particular, I would require the very words in which the alleged blunder occurs. . . .

*   *   *

I shall be told, however, that the most serious of all the accusations made against Moses is, that he says God made all things in six days. It is true that in our version the fourth commandment says so; but surely this first chapter of Genesis does not. It does, indeed, mention six days — one after each stage of progress, but as if to guard against error, it is added in the fourth verse of the next chapter, that God made all things in one day. Without attempting now to explain — for no one can properly comprehend the days until he has long and diligently studied the other parts of this narrative — I will barely mention two facts: 1. The preposition "in" occurs before the word "day" in verse 4, chap. ii; and 2. It does not occur before the "six days" of the commandment. The Hebrew scholar can easily see for himself whether this is so. The English student will notice that the word is placed in italics in the fourth commandment. Whatever may be said as to the meaning of this, one thing is certain, *Genesis* does not *say* that all things were made "*in* six days," and hence the opposer of this account must withdraw or, at least, modify that charge.

If we stopped here, whatever we might gain by clearing away rubbish which others have gathered about this story, our victory would be but half won. Dealing with scientists supposed to be familiar with the history of our world as astronomy, geology, optics, and chemistry have revealed it, I would turn their weapons upon themselves and ask, Was there a beginning to the heavens and the earth? Was God — or, if you please, the great First Cause — their Creator? Was the earth once without form and void? Yes, or no? Did darkness cover the deep before there was motion? Was it God that imparted motion? Was not light the first visible effect of motion? Was not light "good?" Did not God, by means of the solid opaque earth, divide between the light and the darkness? And, after that, was not the light properly and justly called day, and the darkness night? And, until this had been done, although our earth had long revolved upon its axis, giving light as does the sun, was there the alternation which we call day and night? Was not the very first day after that separation really and strictly the *first* day on our globe?

And then, after this had been done, our earth being yet hot, and the ocean yet in the air as dense vapor, was not the next step needed to prepare the world for life — the thinning out of those massive clouds, and the depositing of the water, and so making an open expanse between the clouds floating, as now, in the upper air and the waters beneath? When after this process the blue sky, with the stars and moon and sun, could be seen, what wrong to call it, as we do now, "the heavens?" Thanks to chemistry and geology, we know that the atmosphere in those early times, although clear and transparent, was loaded with carbonic acid and other invisible but poisonous gases, rendering it utterly unfit for respiration. Was or was not Moses right when he withheld from this stage of God's work the verdict of "good?"

In this manner I might go through this account, but these few verses, at which I have been able only as it were to glance, must suffice. I add only one more thought to what has already grown to undue dimensions for a newspaper article.

The physical statements which Moses has recorded are not of a kind whose truth or falsehood is a matter of curiosity merely. No propositions were ever made of more vital importance to science itself. If the earth *never* was without form and void, it never was in a nebulous condition. That would be absolutely impossible. If darkness did not precede motion, then the correlation of forces is a myth. If light did not follow motion, then the undulatory theory is absolutely false. I cannot take more space to set forth these dependencies of science upon the literal truth of these statements, but enough has been said to give some hint of the infinite wealth of knowledge possessed by their real Author and to show that the successful denial of these few opening verses, were that possible, would result most disastrously to science itself.

I, for one, shall continue to believe that the first chapter of Genesis is the most opposite of "poetical, symbolical, and unchronological" that the human mind can conceive. When once we begin to comprehend its full weight of meaning, we

shall find it the most unanswerable of all arguments for miracles and revelation, for it is itself both a miracle and a revelation.

JOHN FISKE

Herbert Spencer's Service to Religion, *Essays Historical and
Literary, New York, 1902, II, pp. 232–237*

All religions agree in the two following assertions, one of
which is of speculative and one of which is of ethical importance. One of them serves to sustain and harmonize our
thoughts about the world we live in, and our place in that
world; the other serves to uphold us in our efforts to do each
what we can to make human life more sweet, more full of
goodness and beauty, than we find it. The first of these assertions is the proposition that the things and events of the world
do not exist or occur blindly or irrelevantly, but that all, from
the beginning to the end of time, and throughout the furthest
sweep of illimitable space, are connected together as the orderly manifestations of a divine Power, and that this divine
Power is something outside of ourselves, and upon it our own
existence from moment to moment depends. The second of
these assertions is the proposition that men ought to do certain
things, and ought to refrain from doing certain other things;
and that the reason why some things are wrong to do and
other things are right to do is in some mysterious, but very
real, way connected with the existence and nature of this
divine Power, which reveals itself in every great and every
tiny thing, without which not a star courses in its mighty
orbit, and not a sparrow falls to the ground. Matthew Arnold
once summed up these two propositions very well when he
defined God as "an eternal Power, not ourselves, that makes
for righteousness." This twofold assertion, that there is an
eternal Power that is not ourselves, and that this Power makes
for righteousness, is to be found, either in a rudimentary or in

a highly developed state, in all known religions. . . . I said, a moment ago, that modern civilized men will all acknowledge that this two-sided assertion, in which all religions agree, is of far greater importance than any of the superficial points in which religions differ. It is really of much more concern to us that there is an eternal Power, not ourselves, that makes for righteousness, than that such a Power is onefold or threefold in its metaphysical nature, or that we ought not to play cards on Sunday, or to eat meat on Friday. No one, I believe, will deny so simple and clear a statement as this. But it is not only we modern men, who call ourselves enlightened, that will agree to this. I doubt not even the narrow-minded bigots of days now happily gone by would have been made to agree to it if they could have had some doggedly persistent Socrates to cross-question them. . . . What men in past times have really valued in their religion has been the universal twofold assertion that there is a God, who is pleased with the sight of the just man and is angry with the wicked every day, and when men have fought with one another, and murdered or calumniated one another for heresy about the Trinity or about eating meat on Friday, it has been because they have supposed belief in the non-essential doctrines to be inseparably connected with belief in the essential doctrine. In spite of all this, however, it is true that in the mind of the uncivilized man, the great central truths of religion are so densely over-laid with hundreds of trivial notions respecting dogma and ritual, that his perception of the great central truths is obscure. These great central truths, indeed, need to be clothed in a dress of little rites and superstition, in order to take hold of his dull and untrained intelligence. But in proportion as men become more civilized, and learn to think more accurately, and to take wider views of life, just so do they come to value the essential truths of religion more highly, while they attach less and less importance to superficial details.

Having thus seen what is meant by the essential truths of religion, it is very easy to see what the attitude of the doctrine

of evolution is toward these essential truths. It asserts and
reiterates them both; and it asserts them not as dogmas handed
down to us by priestly tradition, not as mysterious intuitive
convictions of which we can render no account to ourselves,
but as scientific truths concerning the innermost constitution
of the universe — truths that have been disclosed by observation and reflection, like other scientific truths, and that accordingly harmonize naturally and easily with the whole body
of our knowledge. The doctrine of evolution asserts, as the
widest and deepest truth which the study of nature can disclose to us, that there exists a power to which no limit in time
or space is conceivable, and that all the phenomena of the universe, whether they be what we call material or what we call
spiritual phenomena, are manifestations of this infinite and
eternal Power. Now this assertion, which Mr. Spencer has so
elaborately set forth as a scientific truth — nay, as the ultimate truth of science, as the truth upon which the whole
structure of human knowledge philosophically rests — this
assertion is identical with the assertion of an eternal Power,
not ourselves, that forms the speculative basis of all religions.
When Carlyle speaks of the universe as in very truth the star-
dome city of God, and reminds us that through every crystal
and through every grass blade, but most through every living
soul, the glory of a present God still beams, he means pretty
much the same thing that Mr. Spencer means, save that he
speaks with the language of poetry, with language coloured
by emotion, and not with the precise, formal, and colourless
language of science. By many critics who forget that names
are but the counters rather than the hard money of thought,
objections have been raised to the use of such a phrase as the
Unknowable, whereby to describe the power that is manifest
in every event of the universe. Yet, when the Hebrew prophet
declared that "by him were laid the foundations of the deep,"
but reminded us "Who by searching can find him out?" he
meant pretty much what Mr. Spencer means when he speaks
of a power that is inscrutable in itself, yet is revealed from

moment to moment in every throb of the mighty rhythmic life of the universe.

And this brings me to the last and most important point of all. What says the doctrine of evolution with regard to the ethical side of this twofold assertion that lies at the bottom of all religion? Though we cannot fathom the nature of the inscrutable Power that animates the world, we know, nevertheless, a great many things that it does. Does this eternal Power, then, work for righteousness? Is there a divine sanction of holiness and a divine condemnation for sin? Are the principles of right living really connected with the intimate constitution of the universe? If the answer of science to these questions be affirmative, then the agreement with religion is complete, both on the speculative and on the practical side; and that phantom which has been the abiding terror to timid and superficial minds — that phantom of the hostility between religion and science — is exorcised now and forever. Now, science began to return a decisively affirmative answer to such questions as these when it began, with Mr. Spencer, to explain moral beliefs and moral sentiments as products of evolution. For clearly, when you say of a moral belief or a moral sentiment, that it is a product of evolution, you imply that it is something which the universe through untold ages has been labouring to bring forth, and you ascribe to it a value proportionate to the enormous effort it has cost to produce it. Still more, when with Mr. Spencer we study the principles of right living as part and parcel of the whole doctrine of the development of life upon the earth; when we see that in an ultimate analysis that is right which tends to enhance fulness of life, and that is wrong which tends to detract from fulness of life — we then see that the distinction between right and wrong is rooted in the deepest foundations of the universe; we see that the very same forces, subtle, and exquisite, and profound, which brought upon the scene the primal germs of life and caused them to unfold, which through countless ages of struggle and death has cherished the life that could live more perfectly and destroyed the life that could only live less perfectly, until humanity, with all its hopes, and fears, and aspirations, has come into being as the crown of all this stupendous work — we see that these very same subtle and exquisite forces have wrought into the very fibres of the universe those principles of right living which it is man's highest function to put into practice. The theoretical sanction thus given to right living is incomparably the most powerful that has ever been assigned in any philosophy of ethics. Human responsibility is made more strict and solemn than ever, when the eternal Power that lives in every event of the universe is thus seen to be in the deepest possible sense the author of the moral law that should guide our lives, and in obedience to which lies our only guarantee of the happiness which is incorruptible — which neither inevitable misfortune nor unmerited obloquy can ever take away. I have but barely touched upon a rich and suggestive topic. When this subject shall once have been expounded and illustrated with due thoroughness — as I earnestly hope it will be within the next few years — then I am sure it will be generally acknowledged that our great teacher's services to religion have been no less signal than his services to science, unparalleled as these have been in all the history of the world.

CHAPTER 6 The Accommodation
to Social Thought

Despite the presence of William Graham Sumner, and the now popular identification of "social Darwinism" with his own brutally literal applications of a struggle for existence to human society, the typical social accommodation was not Neo-Darwinian, but Neo-Lamarckian. In fact, Sumner himself could better be regarded as a classical economist than as a Darwinian, for it was Malthus's law of population, not biological speculation, which was basic to his thought. But whatever the origin of his thought, Sumner was an isolated figure who does not belong in the present story. As the first selection following indicates, even Americans who made free use of such a term as "survival of the fittest" — and who seemed to glory in its bloodiest applications, still managed to derive an exuberantly cheerful doctrine from it. The anonymous writer exemplifies both a religious and a social attitude which one could label "overaccommodation," a frequently encountered reaction in both areas of thought. Hastily and uncritically seizing upon some scientific doctrine, in this case that of the survival of the fittest, such writers generally found that it confirmed their most cherished hopes.

The inheritance of acquired characters, as an earlier selection from Joseph LeConte indicated, was an essential part of

American social thought during the last quarter of the nineteenth century. It was a doctrine subscribed to by even such writers as Richard Dugdale, whose classic *The Jukes* (1875) was used by a later generation to demonstrate the genetic determination of antisocial traits. Such a use, however, amounted to turning Dugdale on his head, for his own conclusions were in the more comfortable Lamarckian tradition: ". . . the logical induction seems to be that environment is the ultimate controlling factor in determining careers, placing heredity itself as an organized result of invariable environment."

In other words, an altered environment would have redeemed even the Jukes.

Among the earliest exponents of social evolution based on Neo-Lamarckianism was John Wesley Powell (1834–1902), an explorer, geologist and ethnologist who held several high positions in government science. Adopting the "mental determinants" of Cope and the American school of evolution, Powell argued that essentially new factors were introduced when man came on the evolutionary scene. Man's evolution being a product of human invention and human choice, his further evolution is presumably unlimited. It is difficult to conceive of a more comforting doctrine for a social reformer.

ANONYMOUS

Survival of the Fittest, *The Christian Advocate, New York, March 20, 1879*

Some accepting the doctrine of the survival of the fittest, consider it logical to deny eternal punishment. Long before the Analogy was written, men received in their hearts the harmonious unity coming from nature and revelation. What is heaven but the company of the fittest? Only a few of the best men reach that promised land. Faith, love, all the high virtues, immortalize the saved. His attributes, flowing from God, are eternal. By their nature they make the saved happy, escape pain, decay, death. The very laws of salvation in the universe work together, that the man of God may survive. He is the fittest on earth to survive. He triumphs over enemies without and within, even death itself. What plant or animal compares with him in fitness for survival in the struggle for life? The survival of the fittest cattle is wonderful. The old and less useful forms are left hungry in the stables of the poor, or perish from the earth. The improved ones grow up as calves of the stall, always fat. They are in high repute in the favor of the people. The poorer breeds are found no more in the great expositions, where only the fittest survive. So wide is the sway of this principle, that the worse inanimate machine is cast away to make room for the better. It is wisdom among men to conserve every moment the fittest. God taught our fathers that the best, the fittest, will survive forever in his presence. Over the wrecks of time His name has come to us.

All glory and honor and wisdom and power unto Him who selects, approves, rewards, conserves the best. What a blessing to let the unreformed drunkard and his children die, and not increase them above all others. How incalculable the pain in his billions of offspring, if vice and misery survive, and virtue and pleasure die, How wise to let those of weak digestion from gluttony die, and the temperate live. What benevolence to let the lawless perish, and the prudent survive. How charitable for the warlike to fall by violence, and the meek to inherit the earth. It is a great law of nature and of grace that he who obeys best, survives the fittest. One who obeys all the physical laws of nature lives longer, happier himself, gives to his children an improved constitution. So from the hour he begins to walk with God he obtains a better inheritance, and finds in his own soul the conservation of all his best energies, the survival of the fittest. His evil thoughts, bad inclinations,

enmities, fears, are eternally lost. They will never return.
They are not the fittest for him. They do not survive.* Halle-
luiah to our God, who makes and keeps the better and separates
the worse! He does it in nature and in grace. As the scientist
wants all pure truth in his science, so God wants all true and
holy in heaven. The separation of the evil and good is a
necessity in life and thought. The wilted plant has perished
with the first sun. The grass is eaten by the ox for a higher
being. The worms are living for the birds, the mouse for the
owl. The worse is in pain, death. It meets every faculty of the
true man that the world shall be better. Then the fittest survives, and forever. What lost, extinct race of beasts ever re-
vives itself, or again runs its chance in probation?

"These shall go away into ever-lasting punishment: but the
righteous into life eternal."

The highest and most rigid scientific induction supports the
orthodox faith.

J O H N   W E S L E Y   P O W E L L
The Three Methods of Evolution, *Presidential Address before the
Philosophical Society of Washington, December 8, 1883, in Smith-
sonian Miscellaneous Collections, XXXIII, 1888, pp. xlvii–lii*

If attention is directed exclusively to animal life, we notice
that evolution has proceeded *pari passu* with specialization.
Of the forms that have been specialized from time to time some
have become extinct, some have been degraded, and some have
been evolved in varying degree. One form, not the most specialized, made the greatest progress in evolution, until an organism
was developed of so high a grade that this species became more
independent of environment than any other, and, by reason of

---

* The foregoing paragraph is a particularly good statement of "Social
Darwinism." Note that the writer's point of view, like that of most
so-called "Social Darwinists," was Neo-Lamarckian, including both
individual effort and the inheritance of acquired characteristics.

its superiority, spread widely throughout the land portion of the globe. This superior animal was early man, when he first inhabited all the continents and the great islands. The production of this superior, i.e., more highly systematized organism, was the antecedent to the inauguration of new methods of evolution.

It has been shown that the great efficiency of the biotic method of evolution by survival depends upon competition for existence in enormously overcrowded populations. Man, having acquired superiority to other animals, passed beyond the stage when he had to compete with them for existence upon the earth and into the stage where he could utilize plants and animals alike for his own purposes. They could no longer crowd him out, and to that extent the law of the survival of the fittest in the struggle for existence was annulled in its application to man. He artificially multiplies such of the lower animals as are most useful to him, and domesticates them, that they may be more thoroughly under his control, and modifies them, that they may be more useful, and uses such as he will for beasts of burden; and the wild beasts he destroys from the face of the earth. In like manner he cultivates useful plants, and destroys such as are worthless to him. He does not compete with other biotic species, but utilizes them for his welfare. Yet the law of the survival of the fittest applies insofar as it is not dependent upon competition, and slow evolution may still result therefrom. But at this stage new methods spring up of such great efficiency that the method by the survival of the fittest may be neglected because of its insignificance.

In anthropic combinations the units are men, and men at this stage are no longer passive objects, but active subjects; and instead of man being passively adapted to the environment, he adapts the environment to himself through his activities. This is the essential characteristic of anthropic evolution. Adaptation becomes active instead of passive. In this change certain parts of the human organism are increasingly exercised from generation to generation. This steadily increasing exercise results in steadily increasing development, and the progress of the unit — man — in this higher organization depends upon development through exercise. But the progress by exercise depends upon the evolution of activities.

Man is an animal, and may be studied as such; and this branch of science belongs to biology. But man is more than an animal. Though an animal in biotic function, he is man in his anthropic activities; for by them men are combined — i.e., interrelated — so that they are not discrete beings, but each acts on, for, and with, his fellow-man in the pursuit of happiness. Human activities, thus combined and organized, transcend the activities of the lower animals to such a degree as to produce a new kingdom of matter. The nature of these activities must here be set forth.

The first grand class is composed of those which affect the external world, and by them men are interrelated through their desires. These activities are the Arts. The arts have been evolved by human invention, and man has been impelled thereto by his endeavor to supply his wants. In the course of the evolution of the arts, man has progressively obtained control over the materials and powers of nature. All the arts of all the human period are the inventions of men. But invention has proceeded by minute increments of growth. A vast multiplicity of arts have been devised, of which comparatively few survive in the highest civilization. As the inventions have been made, the best in the average has been chosen. Man has therefore exercised choice. The evolution of the arts has thus been by the method of invention and choice, in the endeavor to gratify desire, and by them man has adapted the environment to himself.

Second. There is a grand class of activities through which men are interrelated in respect to their conduct. These activities result in Institutions. Through them men are associated for a variety of purposes. . . .

*   *   *

Institutions have been developed from extreme simplicity to extreme complexity. They are all the inventions of mankind, and their evolution has been by minute increments of growth. Their invention has been wrought out that men might live together in peace and render one another assistance; and gradually, by the consideration of particulars of conduct as they have arisen from time to time, men have sought to establish justice, that they might thereby secure peace. Of the vast multiplicity of institutions — forms of state, forms of government, and provisions of law — which have been invented, but few remain in the highest civilization, and these few have been selected by men. Men have thus exercised choice. Institutions, therefore, have been developed by invention and the choice of the just in the endeavor to secure peace.

Third. There is another fundamental group of activities through which men are interrelated in respect to their thoughts. These are the activities of mental intercommunication, and result in Languages. Languages, also, are inventions by minute increments of growth. Many languages have been invented, and in each language many words and many methods of combining linguistic devices have been invented. In the languages of the most civilized peoples, but few of these survive; and there are spoken by all the peoples of the earth but few languages in comparison to the many that existed in the early history of mankind; and the method of survival, when analyzed, is found also to be choice. Men have chosen the economic in the expression of thought. Languages, therefore, have developed by invention and choice in the struggle for expression.

Fourth. There is a grand class of activities by which men are interrelated in respect to their designs. Men arrive at Opinions, and these have always reacted upon languages, institutions, and arts, and largely led them in their courses of progress. Because of their opinions, men are willing to work together, and thus have common designs. There have been many opinions and many systems of philosophy. Of all that have existed, but few remain in the highest civilization. A careful analysis of the facts relating to the growth of opinions reveals this truth, that opinions also are invented, and that the final survival of the few has been due to the human act of choice in the selection of the truth. Opinions, therefore, have been developed by invention and choice in the struggle to know.

Fifth. Opinions are formed as the direct activities of the Mind. Languages, institutions, and arts have arisen through the action of the mind and the exercise of other corporeal functions. All these activities, therefore, are dependent upon the mind. On the other hand, these objective activities react upon the mind, so that mental operations are controlled thereby. Through the exercise of the mind in the prosecution of activities it is developed. These mental activities are perception and comparison, or reflection, as it is more usually called. The subjective evolution of the mind is therefore the product of the objective evolution of activities.

These five great classes of activities are interdependent in such a manner that one is not possible without the others; they arise together, and their history proceeds by a constant interchange of effects. All the five classes of activities react upon man as an animal in such a manner that his biotic history subsequent to his differentiation from the lower animals is chiefly dependent thereon. The evolution of man as a being superior to the beast is therefore due to the organization of activities.

It has been shown that man does not compete with the lower animals for existence. In like manner, man does not compete with man for existence; for by the development of activities men are interdependent in such a manner that the welfare of one depends upon the welfare of others; and as men discover that welfare must necessarily be mutual, egoism is transmuted into altruism, and moral sentiments are developed which become the guiding principles of mankind. So morality repeals the law of the survival of the fittest in the struggle for existence, and man is thus immeasurably superior to the beast. In animal evolution many are sacrificed for the benefit of the few. Among mankind the welfare of one depends upon the welfare of all, because interdependence has been established.

It has thus been shown that there are three stages in the combination of matter and motion, and that each stage is characterized by a clearly distinct method of evolution. These may be defined as follows:

First, physical evolution is the result of direct adaptation to environment, under the law that motion is in the direction of least resistance.

Second, biotic evolution is the result of indirect adaptation to the environment by the survival of the fittest in the struggle for existence.

Third, anthropic evolution is the result of the exercise of human faculties in activities designed to increase happiness, and through which the environment is adapted to man.

These may be briefly denominated: evolution by adaptations, evolution by survival of the fittest, and evolution by endeavor.

Civilized men have always recognized to some extent the laws of human evolution, — that activities are teleologically developed, and that happiness is increased thereby. . . . When man loses faith in himself, and worships nature, and subjects himself to the government of the laws of physical nature, he lapses into stagnation, where mental and moral miasm is bred. All that makes man superior to the beast is the result of his own endeavor to secure happiness.

Man, so far as he is superior to the beast, is the master of his own destiny, and not the creature of the environment. He adapts the natural environment to his wants, and thus creates an environment for himself. . . . Man lives in the desert by guiding a river thereon and fertilizing the sands with its waters, and the desert is covered with fields and gardens and homes. Everywhere he rises superior to physical nature. The angry sea may not lash him with its waves, for on the billows he builds a palace, and journeys from land to land. When the storm rises it is signaled from afar, and he gathers his loved ones under the shelter of his home, and they listen to the melody of the rain upon the roof. When the winds of winter blow he kindles fossil sunshine on his hearth, and sings the song of the Ingleside. When night covers the earth with darkness he illumines his path with lightning light. For disease he discovers antidote, for pain nepenthe, and he gains health and long life by sanitation; and ever is he utilizing the materials of nature, and ever controlling its powers. By his arts, institutions, languages, and philosophies he has organized a new kingdom of matter, over which he rules. The beasts of the field, the birds of the air, the denizens of the waters, the winds, the waves, the rivers, the seas, the mountains, the valleys, are his subjects; the powers of nature are his servants, and the granite earth his throne.

CHAPTER 7   A Scientist
                                      Changes His Mind

This section contains, as a case study in a scientific change of
mind, two articles by Alexander Winchell, a prominent geologist connected at various times with Vanderbilt University,
the University of Michigan, and Syracuse University. The
first, written in 1863, is a popular — although quite sophisti-
cated — argument against all "development" theories in general and against Darwinism in particular. The second, written
in 1877, is an argument in favor of evolution, along with
Winchell's assurance that he has not been overly hasty in
reaching this conviction. Were the difficulties he found in
1863 really resolved fourteen years later? Was he simply persuaded by the weight of the evidence? Or had he decided
that other issues were more important? I think the answers to
these questions are ambiguous and will depend upon the weight
which one gives to Winchell's explanations. The reason why a
scientist, faced with two theories covering the same facts, opts
for one rather than the other, has thus far defied any certain
analysis, and will probably be found to vary from one individual to the next. Certainly the "antecedent probability"
which William North Rice assigned to a naturalistic explanation over a supernatural one was a powerful argument in favor
of evolution, and one that could often overcome a lack of
visible evidence. It should be noted, however, that Winchell

expressed his preference for the Neo-Lamarckian mode of evolution, and also that even in 1863 he did not think that the establishment of a theory of evolution would prove dangerous to religion.

ALEXANDER   WINCHELL
Voices from Nature, *The Ladies' Repository, July 1863, pp. 387–390*

XIX. *"Development" Theories*

The theory of Darwin in his "Origin of Species by Means of Natural Selection" is the latest, and by far the ablest and most formidable of all. Without alleging the spontaneous origin of life, and without *assuming*, as Lamarck and the "Vestiges" do, that an inherent tendency to improvement exists in nature, Darwin appeals to the tendency of external conditions, which are admitted on all hands. With him the conflicts continually occurring among animals and plants in their struggle for life, necessitate the ascendency of the stronger and more perfect; so that only the best of each generation survive to continue their kind. . . . This theory, like the others, obliterates the permanent distinction of species. Every type is but a passing phase. Man himself was not created man, but is only the last grist ground out by that stupendous system of machinery which, without attention, without intervention, without design, without intelligence, elaborates the most complicated organisms, effects the most wonderful adjustments, produces the most consummate and admirable adaptations, and in its every feature and evolution presents phenomena so surpassing in their indications of a supreme Intelligence, that a false philosophy attempts to deny in it the existence of all intelligence.

XX. *Objections to All "Development" Theories . . .*

*   *   *

1. *As to the spontaneous origin of life.* [Winchell lists objections, but he recognizes that Darwin's theory does not assume spontaneous generation.]

2. *The succession of organic forms is sometimes retrogressive instead of progressive.* Among articulates the most ancient type is that of Trilobites. This type, though not high in the sub-kingdoms, is, nevertheless, far from standing at the bottom, and, according to the development theories, should have been preceded by the Entomostracans. Instead of this, the Entomostracans follow in later ages, mostly after Trilobites have disappeared. Insects, likewise, on their first appearance were represented by weevils, beetles, locusts, dragon-flies, ants, and cockroaches simultaneously — forms belonging to five of the higher orders. Subsequently the lower types came into being. The earlier fishes belonged to types which are generally regarded as superior to our ordinary fishes. . . . Lastly the class of mammals seems to have experienced a similar dwindling just before the advent of man. The retrenchment of bulk does not always imply degradation of rank, but among *closely-related species* bulk is regarded as a criterion of the relative amount of vital force.

3. *Higher and lower types were in many cases simultaneously introduced.* . . . What chance existed for the development of an *Orthoceras* from a *Lingula*, when the two made their appearance upon the earth in the same epoch, it seems very difficult to perceive — or, rather, it is easy to perceive that the chance was infinitely small. In the earliest stages of the empire of fishes, the reptile *Telerpeton Elginense* came upon the stage of being, and the fishes went on afterward in their acquisition of sauroid characteristics and other concomitants of higher development, without any regard to the fact that the reptilian type had been already supplied, and no slow and secular development of it was needed. In a similar way

Triassic mammals thrust themselves into the company of the reptiles which were not yet half prepared for transmutation into birds, still less into mammals. Finally, in the first stage of Cenozoic time, monkeys, the highest type of mammals below man, made their advent in company with the first mammalian fauna the world ever saw, without the least regard to the requirements of Lamarck or Darwin.

4. *Certain Class-types were abruptly introduced upon the earth.* The very first fauna which ever existed — reasoning from geological data thus far ascertained — made its appearance without any of that preparation required by development theories. The class of Brachiopods should have been preceded by that of Bryozoa and Foraminifera, the hard tests [e.g., shell-like covering] of which would have been much more likely of preservation than the fragile shells of *Lingula* and *Obolella*. Fishes burst upon the world without being heralded by a single prophetic type; and insects, as we have seen, fluttered in all their higher orders, without the intervention of any of those preparatory types which announced the coming of reptiles, and ammonites, and many other grades of being.

5. *The geological series is sometimes interrupted.* Links are sometimes wanting where it is not a sufficient explanation to say that future researches may bring them to light. The gap existing between man and the Quadrumana is an example of the kind. To say nothing of the vast interval separating them in mental and moral characteristics, the structural disparity leaves room for the insertion of several intermediate grades. A similar interruption exhibits itself in organological development. If the history of animals has been a progressive development, then organs appropriate to lower grades of being have been successively laid aside and replaced by organs appropriate to higher grades. For instance, the carnivorous type of dentition is universally regarded as higher than the herbivorous; and an adaption to terrestrial life, a more exalted endowment than the gift of swimming. Now, when the mammalian series had been developed upward from the whale

through the terrestrial horse and ox to the carnivorous and terrestrial wolf, who can explain, on development principles, how the seal, which is allied to the wolf in its dentition, happens to fall back again to the grade of the whale in its aquatic style of locomotion? Or who would have expected that the class of mammals, having left off the characteristics of birds, and having been developed into its higher and more complicated forms, should, in the bats, return to that aerial mode of locomotion which characterizes birds and insects?

6. *Certain types have been interpolated in time, between two closely-related types.* This principle is illustrated by the *Labyrinthodonts* and amphicoelian crocodiles of the coal measures, the Permian and Trias, which intervene, in time, between the sauroid fishes of the mountain limestone and the saurian reptiles of the Jurassic and Cretaceous periods, from which they are named. Now, if the sauroid element of the fish was but the evidence of an inherent struggle of nature for a higher style of organization, why did not the fish pass at once into the true saurian instead of the bucklered frog and fish-like crocodile? From the epoch of the coal measures till the dawn of the Lias, the saurian type was detained in the vestibule of creation, while frogs and salamanders crowded into the temple of life and entertained the "principle of development" for a whole geological age after the drama of saurians had been placarded, and the engagement emphasized by the assurance of "no postponement." So when the whale-like Ichthyosaurian had excited expectations of the advent of cetacean monsters, behold he is followed by some gigantic lizards, and the whales have to bide their time. If this is "development," it is a very rough and a very crooked road.

7. *Certain organic types have remained unchanged from remote geological periods.* In the very first fauna which existed on our globe were the two genera, *Lingula* and *Discina*. Those genera have reappeared in almost every geological age to the present; and, contrary to the rule in every other case, may be collected in existing seas. Is there any evidence of

development here? Is development compatible with the facts? Before the close of the Palaezoic period there had appeared on the earth seventeen genera of molluscs, which have survived to the present. One single species, *Atrypa reticularis*, is known to have lived in eleven successive epochs . . . *Strophomena rhomboidalis* is thought to range even from the Lower Silurian to the Carboniferous. Besides such persistence of generic and specific characters, we have the fact that all the class and ordinal groups, and most of the family groups, have persisted unaltered, through many geological aeons, and exhibit to-day the same restriction of characters as they did in Palaeozoic or Mesozoic times. We are, therefore, fully justified in concluding that a specific, generic, family, ordinal, or class-type is a definite, well-circumscribed, and original creation — a primordial form, which is reproduced with the same fidelity as a crystal of quartz or calcareous spar.

8. *Development theories do not account for the genesis of new organs.* We can easily understand how, when the rudiments of a visual organ, for instance, have been implanted, a principle of development may be supposed to improve and perfect it. But could such a principle create the rudiments? Now the mechanism of an eye, however rudimentary, is extremely unlike any other structure, both in its anatomy and in its functions. What can be found, then, in the eyeless monad, or earth-worm, or lamp shell, which our theorist would expect to see developed into the eye-spots of the oyster, the ocelli of the spider, or the visual organ of a cuttle-fish? The same difficulty exists in the supposed development of the other senses, and indeed of nearly all the organs which characterize the higher grades of life; for the simplest forms of animalization are quite destitute of special organs of any kind.

9. *Existing species appear to be immutable.* Not only are no transmutations going on before our own eyes, but we know that from the earliest periods of written history no perceptible modifications have been wrought in the species of animals exhumed from the tombs of the ancient Egyptians. The savans

attached to the French army in its occupation of Egypt, sent home in great numbers the embalmed bodies of consecrated animals, such as the bull, the dog, the cat, the ape, the ichneumon, the crocodile, and the ibis. The collections were submitted to the scrutiny of the professors of the Museum of Natural History at Paris, and they presented a report, in which they say, "We can scarcely restrain the transports of our imagination, on beholding thus presented, with their minutest bones, with the smallest portions of their skin, and in every particular most perfectly recognizable, many an animal, which at Thebes or Memphis, two or three thousand years ago, had its own priests and altars." There was the domestic cat, for example, which in the vicissitudes of two or three thousand years ago, in being transported over every meridian and into every clime, with the principle of development still inherent, and the struggle of individuals and varieties for supremacy all the time vigorously kept up, has not improved one iota upon the cats which purred in the temples of the ancient Egyptians. Alas for the cats! There seems to be little chance of their rising to the respectability of monkeys. When, then, will they begin to build steamboats, and gaze at the stars, and speculate on their own genealogy?

We have merely shown the nature of the facts which militate against those theories which deny constancy of species. It would not be appropriate to say more in this place, if propriety allows us even the license we have taken. We dismiss the subject with the following suggestion: Facts are God's facts. God is to be learned by His actions as well as His words; and being perfect He has no where contradicted Himself. If facts hereafter brought to light prove either spontaneous generation or progressive development, then we shall know that these are among God's methods of working. That is all. We shall then be taught that God makes organic creatures by the intervention of laws, just as He makes crystals, and oceans, and worlds. It will then appear that God made man by the slow process of secular development, as He made the continents.

We shall simply remove the First Cause a little further back, without invalidating one jot or one tittle of the sacred Word. But it seems that such theories are *not* facts, and hence to embrace them leads us away from truth and from God.

ALEXANDER   WINCHELL
Grounds and Consequences of Evolution, *Sparks from A Geologist's Hammer, Chicago, S. C. Griggs and Company, 1881, pp. 333–348*

In spite of the objections presented in the last chapter to the breadth of Professor Huxley's claim, we are strongly persuaded that the doctrine of the derivative descent of animal and vegetal forms represents the truth. We discover no conflict between it and the "creation theory." We even maintain that a philosophic scrutiny of the doctrine will disclose the activity of creative power not alone in the region of "external agency," and inaugurative efficiency, but in every stage of that derivation which guides and employs biological forces with reference to preconceived results.

We have not been hasty to reach this conviction. We have pondered many a difficulty and raised many a query, but we have seen old difficulties vanishing and new proofs perpetually arising. We have learned more of the wonderful resources of the hypothesis in explaining the current and the exceptional phenomena of life and organization. We now think it far safer to accept the hypothesis than to reject it. If it is safer for the scientist it is safer for religion. It is therefore time for the theologian to seek how to coordinate his essential faith with the impending finality of science. . . .

*   *   *

There is first, what may be called the *morphological evidence*, or evidence furnished by structural relationships and family resemblances among living animals and plants. Everyone understands what is meant by saying one person bears a family resemblance to another. It implies that there is a blood-connection between them. In some generation more or less remote their lineage converges, and the same parents stand as common ancestors to both persons. Precisely the same thing is involved in the statement that the dog, the wolf and the jackal have a family resemblance, — or the cat, the lynx, the ounce and the panther. The resemblances in these families are not so close as in a human family; but they are of the same kind, and they impress themselves on us in the same way and with the same effect. We have not been accustomed to thinking of the members of the cat-family as having a common descent; but we universally recognize a close relation of structure, form, movements and instincts. Any one who should ask himself how resemblances of structure, form, movements and instincts arise, would at once perceive that they probably imply common ancestry. It is conceivable that separate species so characterized should have had separate origins; but our intelligence inclines to the other explanation. The reason of this is the fact that we are familiar with examples of more intimate family resemblance in cases of known consanguinity. The children of John Smith are quite certain to resemble their parents, and may reproduce predominantly traits of their grandparents or remoter progenitors. It is not needful to suggest similar illustrations throughout the animal and vegetable kingdoms. All our observation and knowledge, therefore, point to consanguinity as the cause of all family resemblances; and we have no knowledge of any other cause of them. There is no ground of hesitation to accept consanguinity as the true explanation, save our preexisting assumption that all distinct specific forms are independent originations; and if we scrutinize this assumption, we perceive that it is held simply because it has been taught us in our childhood. That opinion has been thought demanded by our intuition and traditional belief concerning the relation of Creator and the world; but when it is shown that the demands of this intuition and belief are better satisfied by the admission of a consanguineous relation among animals, it would seem that no ground whatever remains for the old assumption that each species is a separate creation. It is certainly safe, on the grounds of natural evidence, and, as I will attempt to show in the sequel, on the ground of religion, to admit that family resemblances among animals, as among mankind, imply community of descent.

This principle achieved, very much is found involved in it. Resemblances of the same nature as those called family resemblances exist between groups of animals and plants quite widely differentiated from each other. We do not say the mouse and the rhinoceros possess a family resemblance, but it is demonstrable that they do possess profound resemblances aggregating vastly more than all their differences. . . .

*   *   *

If we stray from our starting point so far as to bring an insect or a worm into the comparison, we find still an immense preponderance of resemblances. All the invertebrates, like the vertebrates, possess the faculty of voluntary motion; they hunger and feed; they perceive; they have relations to each other and to the inanimate world; they breathe; they digest; they reproduce; they provide for, protect and defend their young; their whole system of physiological activity and co-ordinated structure is the same; they have mouth, oesophagus, stomach, intestine, liver; they digest by secretion of gastric juice, and imbibe the nutritive products of digestion; they appropriate the oxygen of the air; and aerate a fluid answering to blood; they have nerves which ramify to the various organs; they move by means of contractile muscular fibers; they rest from their labors at certain intervals, and sleep. Certainly, if a genetic relationship unites the different classes of vertebrates, it must also embrace the other animals which possess such a preponderance of resemblances with the vertebrates.

All classification is based on these resemblances. Classification, if true and correct, is therefore nothing more than the building of a genealogical tree.

There are numerous independent features of the morphological evidence. . . . The splint-bones of the horse's foot are, beyond all question, the rudiments of additional digits, — either digits in process of development, in the course of generations, or digits in process of disappearance. So the bird has a rudimentary thumb attached to the angle of its wing. Of the same nature is the stumpy caudal extremity of the bird's spinal column, the styloid prolongation of that of the frog, or even the os coccygis of the human subject. Here, as in many other instances, are structures which are rudimental, and perform no function, or only a greatly modified function, in the economy of the animal; while they are manifestly the same morphological elements or combinations as in other animals execute important and often essential functions. What do they mean? On the hypothesis of independent specific creations, it is necessary to suppose the Creator has introduced again and again certain parts which are functionally useless. On the principle that structures are adapted to ends, how are structures *without an end* to be brought under the rule of special creation? But now, if the theory of common genetic descent is admissible, all mystery vanishes. With progressive changes in the physical surroundings and necessities of the line of generations, some structures became more important, more exercised, and more developed, while others became less important, less exercised, and less developed; and some finally shrank to mere non-functional rudiments of their former selves.

Thus the world of contemporaneous existence affords ground for the inference that all existing animals are bound in a genetic system by the bonds of universal cousinship. It is of no import that we revolt at the thought. Perhaps the revulsion has no more rational foundation than taboo among savages. Perhaps the relationship, on reflection, will enhance to a sublime degree our comprehension of the system of organic life, and of the unity of all the world under the method of one intelligence. Perhaps it will appear that man's structure was not embraced in the scheme of derivative origins. Perhaps, if it was so embraced, he will be found to possess some distinct elements in his psychic nature which cannot be traced to lower existences. In any event, having felt the force of the evidence, it is manly to stand by it, and let the unity of truth determine the adjustment of the consequences.

We have, in the second place, what may be styled the *palaeontological evidence*. The discovered records of extinct life upon the earth, it must be admitted, are extremely defective, and offer many instances which, in the present state of our knowledge, appear to conflict with the doctrine of descent, though there are no facts irreconcilable with it. That the record is incomplete, and must always remain incomplete, is obvious from a few considerations. . . .

* * *

In spite of all this, palaeontology has been able to establish the following principles:

1. There has been a *gradual improvement* in the structural rank of the leading types of animals as the history advanced from age to age.

2. The earlier condition of each animal type was a *comprehensive* one, in which certain characteristics of two or more later families or orders were united in one species.

3. The tendency of change has been toward the *resolution of comprehensive types*, so that the characteristics of each separate family or order should finally be embodied in separate species.

4. While this process of resolution of comprehensive types has been in progress, still further differentiations and specializations, both in the comprehensive and the resolved forms, have taken place.

5. The progress of discovery has gone so far that we have established not only a steady progression upward in the animal series at large, but also in several separate ramifications of the series.

6. Thus we trace tolerably continuous lines of succession. (a) From typical land saurians upward through Pterosaurs,

Archaeopteryx and *Hesperornis* to Carinate Birds; (b) from typical land saurians upward through *Iguanodon, Hadrosaurus, Compsognathus* and *Brontozoum* to Struthious Birds; though in both these series (only given in part) the types structurally consecutive are not always chronologically ranged in the same order; (c) The Camel series, . . . (d) The Rhinoceros series, . . . (e) The Horse series, . . . — all these chronologically as well as systematically arranged. Also several other series quite fully made out, such as those leading to the Elephant, the Hog, the Deer and the Ox.

7. The tendency of fresh discovery is continually to fill up preexisting gaps. Serial successions are being completed from year to year; connecting links are coming to light; terms once thought misplaced are found, through new discoveries, to be in proper successional order.

In this state of the facts it is perfectly legitimate to forecast results. Induction has established a law from which we may deduce anticipated results. We may reason then from what we expect to know, as well as from what we know.

We anticipate, accordingly, that in the course of time it will be shown that our earth has been the abode of complete successions of animal types, leading backward from each of our modern generic or family groups, by ever-converging lines, toward ancestral centers; and from these centers, other lines pointing toward some common center in the remoter past. We expect to see the consecutive terms in these various series graduating structurally into each other, and every characteristic conformed and arranged *as if* there had been a gradual descent of all our modern mammals, along a set of diverging lines from some primitive, plantigrade, five-toed ancestor.

This is the generalization which the known facts and the known tenor of the facts authorize us to draw. But when we shall have become convinced of the existence of such a complete series of successional lines, we shall not yet have the demonstration of a genealogical connection between any two terms in any series. It will still be supposable, . . . that each term is a separate origination. . . . We may fairly argue that the facts accord with the theory of derivation, and are best explained by that theory, and lend it a high degree of probability; but we should feel our confidence materially strengthened if we could detect nature in the act of effecting a transition from species to species.

We have therefore, in the third place, the *variational evidence*. This consists of a body of facts tending to show that a species is not a primordial and permanent organic form, but only the existing phase presented by a line of progressive changes. Much light has been thrown upon this subject within a few years. Some cases of transmutation have been actually traced, and evidence has been gained that the gradational series connecting species of animals and plants, long regarded distinct, are in truth only transitional states of one of these species in its passage over to the other. . . .

*   *   *

The sum total of the variational evidence shows us that the derivative origin of types in palaeontological history is a natural possibility. We are not in conflict with nature, therefore, in inferring that the terms of the palaeontological series sustain a consanguineous relation.

But in the fourth place we have the *embryological evidence*. This seems to us to bring all the other evidence to a focus and complete the conviction that the derivative origin of species is a fact. It affords not only a picture of the succession of extinct forms, but it is a picture in which the successive terms are *known* to be derivatively related to each other. Trace any higher vertebrate — man himself, if you will — from a primitive condition in the ovum. How marvelous, how awe-inspiring is the unfolding! We have first the yolk, with its "germinative vesicle" and "germinative dot." Then both undergo a succession of segmentations until there results a crowded mass of cells ("morula" or "mulberry" stage). Some of these dissolve, and the remainder arrange themselves as a hollow spheroid consisting of a single layer of cells ("planula" stage). The single layer becomes double, with an opening at one pole of the spheroid ("gastrula" stage); and now appears a thickening on one side, in the midst of which is disclosed the "primitive furrow," afterward to be inclosed and become the spinal marrow. An enlargement is seen at one extremity; this is the forming brain; and the various segments of the brain appear as gentle swellings. At the opposite extremity is a tail. Transverse marks in the middle of the neural furrow indicate the approaching vertebral structures; while certain segments along the place of the neck are seen to receive blood-vessels from the provisional heart, and to sustain completely all the structural relations of the branchial or gill arches in the type of fishes. Arms and legs bud out, — as yet without digits, or they may be viewed as unidigitate, like the limbs of *Lepidosiren*. Stumpy digits afterward appear, like those of the so-called *Cheirotherium* of Triassic times. The face goes by degrees through the conditions seen in low sharks, amphibians and higher vertebrates. Step by step the internal structures advance toward their destined forms, functions and positions. Thus, by a process of repeated differentiations, the complications and special adaptations of the higher vertebrate come into existence.

But what of all this? Very much indeed. This marvelous evolution which we see the higher vertebrate pass through is *absolutely identical* with the embryonic history of every other animal down to a certain point in its development. . . . Thus every vertebrated animal presents us the same primitive furrow, the same cerebral enlargements, the same segmentation, the same caudal continuation, the same vascular area, the same one-chambered heart, the same branchial arches and blood-vessels, the same progressive changes in the development of the brain, the same mode of formation of the enteric and abdominal cavities, the same beginnings of the formation of the face. This identity in embryonic histories may be unexpected; it may be amazing; it may be humiliating; but there is nothing better established in science.

This is not all. There are living creatures which represent these successive stages of embryonic development. There are some so low that they never pass beyond the structure of the egg, — simple cells, often, like some eggs, capable of movement by means of prolongations of their substance. There are some which attain to the morula condition, and then are adult. . . . Thus on, from the lancelet and the lampreys to the sharks, Amphibians, Monotremes, Marsupials, and Lemurs at the bottom of the four-handed animals, we discover living forms which stand forth in the museum of Nature as pictures of the embryonic stages of the highest vertebrate.

Finally, the embryonic series finds its parallel not only in the embryonic history of other animals, and in the adult forms of animals presented as we range up and down the scale of life, but the succession of extinct types, as far as we have read it, presents us with another parallel. . . .

*   *   *

To sum up, we have, it appears, an identical order of succession of organic forms three times repeated. The first appears in the successive transformations of the individual being before it reaches maturity. This succession is *ontogenetic* and *rapid*. It is repeated for every individual which comes to maturity. The second succession is presented in the geological history of extinct life. It is not yet observed to be parallel in all details, but the progress of discovery tends continually to complete the parallel. This succession is *palaeontological* and *slow*. The third succession is presented by the serial order of living animals according to rank. All the terms of the series are coexistent. This succession is *taxonomic* and *simultaneous*. The first succession represents the grand march of the animal kingdom as a whole; it is executed but once. The second succession is an epitome of this, continually rehearsed in the life march of individuals. The third succession is one without relation to time or place; it is ideal; it is a survival of traditions of the past, and condenses the evolutions of ages into one present and perpetual expression. PALAEONTOLOGICAL history exhibits a series in which the continued interpolation of newly discovered terms produces the suspicion of a perfectly graduated and genetic line. It suggests material continuity as a *possibility* and a *promise*. MORPHOLOGICAL relations present such continuity as something which, within the range of observation, is a *fact*, and beyond the range of observation is a *probability*. The phenomena of VARIABILITY reveal a disposition and an aptitude on the part of nature to fulfill the "promise," and make the "probability" completely a "fact." The data of EMBRYOLOGY *demonstrate* that the derivative relation of *such* terms as palaeontology presents is an ever-repeated actuality. Now, with the work completed in the ontogenetic epitome, and with this proof of nature's *method*, and the variational proof of nature's *method* and *means*, it is little stretch of belief to grant that nature pursued the method of derivative originations during the whole period of palaeontological history.

A B C D E F G H I J   5 4 3 2 1 7 0 6 9 8